Fraction
Games & Activities
with Dice!

**Fun and Engaging Activities
to Build Fraction Fluency**

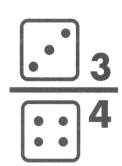

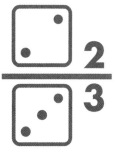

Didax

Rowley, Massachusetts

Printed in the United States of America.

Order Number 211187
ISBN 978-1-58324-737-2

A B C D E 23 22 21 20 19

395 Main Street
Rowley, MA 01969
www.didax.com

Fraction Activities with Dice

Contents

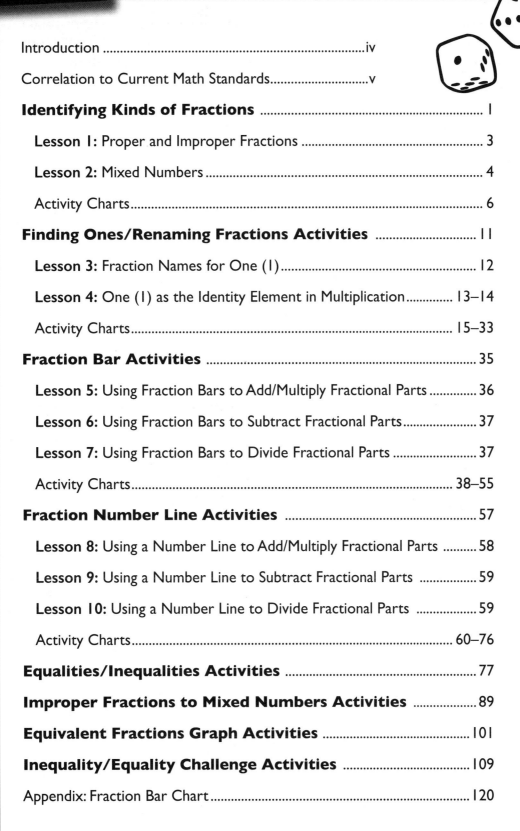

Fraction Activities with Dice – Introduction

Fraction Activities with Dice provides opportunities for students to conceptualize fractions before asking them to apply procedural rules in adding, subtracting, multiplying, and dividing fractions. Conceptual understanding is clearly evident when students can answer the question "What is one-half of 10?" and can use their understanding to solve similar problems, such as one-half of 50, one-half of 100, and so on.

Encouraging students to make connections to what they already know creates a solid mathematical foundation for the introduction of rules such as the algorithm for multiplying fractions—multiplying the numerators and multiplying the denominators. Students should be allowed and encouraged to use their commonsense conceptualizing skills. There is little if any rationale for asking students to solve a given problem using only one "approved" strategy.

For example, students should be encouraged to use the expression "of" as well as "times." "One-half of 10" suggests a cognitive route to solving a problem whereas "one-half times 10" implies a procedure. By the same token, "has how many" invites students to conceptualize division, whereas "divided by" invites students to recall a procedure. If $1 \div \frac{1}{2}$ is interpreted as "One has how many halves?" a student can actually visualize the two halves in an object.

The two strategies (conceptual and procedural) are clearly symbiotic, with one leading to and enhancing the other. Students should be able to rely on conceptual understanding to make sense of a mathematical situation, even when they cannot necessarily recall the correct procedural strategy.

About This Book

The activities in this book are aligned with current mathematical standards and are easily integrated into any commercial program adopted by a school district. Like the other books in the *Dice Activities* series, this book focuses on developing the cognitive and conceptual understanding of number, relationships, and operations. As students participate in the games and activities in this book, they bring the most powerful learning tool known to humans, their minds.

We believe that students should have a facility with number and recall of essential facts and information. We also believe that students develop fluency through play and meaningful experiences.

As important as the "playful" activities in this book are in developing fluency with fractions, teachers' interactions with students, the language they use, and the practices they follow are critical in the development of mathematical minds. Sadly, the teaching of fractions in elementary and middle school is a needlessly unsuccessful experience for many. Best practices continue to inform educators of strategies that work. Such knowledge is reflected in the Notes to Teachers sections that precede each set of activities in this book.

The suggested **scripted lessons** included in these sections lead students to differentiate between kinds of fractions, to understand the identity element for multiplication and division as the basis for creating equivalent fractions, and to employ spatial and linear models when adding, multiplying, subtracting, and dividing fractional parts.

You will note that some activity pages have an icon in the upper left-hand corner with a reference to a specific scripted lesson. This icon serves as a reminder that you can always lead students through a particular lesson again, should they need to review a concept before completing the chart for that page.

The joy of mathematical thinking is an experience that all children deserve, regardless of their mathematical ability. As educators we need to stand firm in our conviction of what children deserve and what it means to be truly educated as a mathematically proficient individual.

The activities in this book have been field-tested with classroom teachers in Sudbury, Wakefield, and Winchester, Massachusetts. As always, we welcome any suggestions for modifications to these activities that will lead to greater mathematical thinking on the part of our students.

—Mary Saltus and Chet Delani

Correlation to Current Math Standards

Standard	Page No.
Grade 3	
Number and Operations – Fractions (3.NF)	
Understand a fraction 1/b as the quantity formed by 1 part when a whole is partitioned into b equal parts; understand a fraction a/b as the quantity formed by a parts of size 1/b. (3.NF.A.1)	6–9
Understand a fraction as a number on the number line; represent fractions on a number line diagram. (3.NF.A.2)	61–76
Understand two fractions as equivalent (equal) if they are the same size, or the same point on a number line. (3.NF.A.3a)	61–76
Recognize and generate simple equivalent fractions, e.g., 1/2 = 2/4, 4/6 = 2/3). Explain why the fractions are equivalent, e.g., by using a visual fraction model. (3.NF.A.3b)	19–33
Express whole numbers as fractions, and recognize fractions that are equivalent to whole numbers. (3.NF.A.3c)	15–16, 19–33
Compare two fractions with the same numerator or the same denominator by reasoning about their size. Recognize that comparisons are valid only when the two fractions refer to the same whole. Record the results of comparisons with the symbols >, =, or <. (3.NF.A.3d)	79–87, 111–119

Correlation to Current Math Standards (cont.)

Grade 4	
Number and Operations – Fractions (4.NF)	
Explain why a fraction a/b is equivalent to a fraction $(n \times a)/(n \times b)$ by using visual fraction models, with attention to how the number and size of the parts differ even though the two fractions themselves are the same size. Use this principle to recognize and generate equivalent fractions. (4.NF.A.1)	19–33, 103–108
Compare two fractions with different numerators and different denominators, e.g., by creating common denominators or numerators, or by comparing to a benchmark fraction such as 1/2. Recognize that comparisons are valid only when the two fractions refer to the same whole. Record the results of comparisons with symbols >, =, or <, and justify the conclusions, e.g., by using a visual fraction model. (4.NF.A.2)	79–87
Understand addition and subtraction of fractions as joining and separating parts referring to the same whole. (4.NF.B.3a)	39–49
Decompose a fraction into a sum of fractions with the same denominator in more than one way ... Justify decompositions, e.g., by using a visual fraction model. (4.NF.B.3b)	39–49
Replace mixed numbers with equivalent fractions. (4.NF.B.3c)	39–49, 91–100, 111–119
Understand a fraction a/b as a multiple of $1/b$. For example, use a visual fraction model to represent 5/4 as the product 5 × (1/4). (4.NF.B.4a)	39–43
Understand a multiple of a/b as a multiple of $1/b$, and use this understanding to multiply a fraction by a whole number. (4.NF.B.4b)	39–43
Grade 5	
Number and Operations – Fractions (5.NF)	
Interpret a fraction as division of the numerator by the denominator ($a/b = a \div b$). (5.NF.B.3)	51–55, 72–76
Apply and extend previous understandings of multiplication to multiply a fraction or whole number by a fraction: Interpret the product $(a/b) \times q$ as a parts of a partition of q into b equal parts; equivalently, as the result of a sequence of operations $a \times q \div b$. (5.NF.B.4a)	51–55
Interpret division of a whole number by a unit fraction, and compute such quotients. (5.NF.B.7b)	72–76

Identifying Kinds
of Fractions

Contents

Notes to Teachers/Identifying Kinds of Fractions

Objective

- Students identify proper fractions, improper fractions, and mixed numbers.

Overview

Students engage in **Four-Grid Tic-Tac-Toe, Four in a Row,** or **Crossover activities** to become familiar with the terms *proper fraction, improper fraction,* and *mixed number.* Before beginning the activities, use **Lesson 1** (next page) to introduce proper and improper fractions and **Lesson 2** to introduce mixed numbers.

Materials

- Dice
- "Identifying Kinds of Fractions" charts (pages 6–9)
- Colored tokens (tiles, cubes, chips)
- Pencils or markers

Getting Started

- Organize students into teams, with two students per team.

- Begin by reviewing with students the definitions listed below.

- Use the scripted lessons on pages 2–4 to assess students' prior knowledge and introduce new concepts.

- Allow time for each team (pair of students) to discuss their thinking and agree on a solution.

- In a large-group discussion, ask student teams to share their thinking.

- Ask if any team had a different way of arriving at the same conclusion.

DEFINITIONS

- A *fraction* is a number that represents one or more parts of a whole.

- The *numerator* is the number above the fraction line. It represents how many parts of the whole are being considered.

- The *denominator* is the nonzero number below the fraction line. It is the total number of equal parts in the whole.

- A *proper fraction* is a fraction in which the numerator is less than the denominator (for example, $\frac{3}{4}$).

- An *improper fraction* is a fraction in which the numerator is greater than or equal to the denominator (for example, $\frac{5}{3}$ and $\frac{6}{6}$).

- A *mixed number* is a whole number and a proper fraction together (for example, $2\frac{2}{3}$).

LESSON 1: PROPER AND IMPROPER FRACTIONS

- Ask: *What is a fraction?* Say: *Whisper your response to your partner.*
- Explore students' responses and list ideas on the board.
- Conclusion: *A fraction is a number that is one or more parts of a whole.*
- List some examples:

$$\frac{3}{4} \qquad \frac{5}{8} \qquad \frac{6}{3} \qquad \frac{2}{5}$$

- Say: *Three of these fractions have something in common. What do you think they have in common?*
- Say: *Whisper to your partner why you made that decision.* Discuss responses.
- Focus on responses that three of the fractions have a smaller numerator than denominator.
- Say: *A fraction that has a smaller numerator than denominator is called a **proper fraction**.*
- Ask: *Which fraction is different from the others?*
- Say: *Whisper to your partner why you made that decision.* Discuss responses.
- Through questioning, lead students to identify an *improper fraction* (a fraction that is more than one whole—i.e., the numerator is larger than the denominator).
- List these fractions on the board:

$$\frac{53}{78} \qquad \frac{250}{100} \qquad \frac{68}{69} \qquad \frac{100,0000}{1,000,000} \qquad \frac{31}{29}$$

- Point to $\frac{53}{78}$. Direct students to give their partner a thumbs-up if $\frac{53}{78}$ is a proper fraction and a thumbs-down if it is not.
- Say: *Whisper to your partner why you made that decision.* Discuss responses.
- Repeat the same procedure with each fraction listed above.
- Ask: *What do you call a fraction that has a smaller numerator than denominator?* (proper fraction)
- Ask: *What do you think a fraction that has a larger numerator than denominator is called?* (improper fraction)
- List these fractions on the board:

$$\frac{15}{9} \qquad \frac{638}{637} \qquad \frac{71}{68} \qquad \frac{46}{55} \qquad \frac{9}{9} \qquad \frac{25}{75} \qquad \frac{32}{32}$$

- Point to each fraction. Direct students to give their partner a thumbs-up if it is an improper fraction and a thumbs-down if it is not.
- Say: *Whisper to your partner why you made that decision.* Discuss responses.
- Students are now ready for the **Proper and Improper Fraction activities** on pages 5–6.

LESSON 2: MIXED NUMBERS

- On the board, list these fractions: $2\frac{2}{3}$ $1\frac{3}{4}$ $\frac{7}{8}$ $4\frac{1}{3}$

- Say: *Three of these fractions have something in common. What do you think they have in common?*

- Say: *Whisper to your partner why you made that decision.*

- Discuss responses.

- Focus on responses that three of the fractions have a whole number combined or "mixed" with a fraction.

- Through questioning, lead students to identify a *mixed number*—i.e., a whole number and a proper fraction together.

- List these fractions on the board:

$$3\frac{2}{8} \qquad \frac{89}{35} \qquad 178\frac{638}{637} \qquad \frac{1000}{758} \qquad 17\frac{81}{82}$$

- Point to each fraction. Direct students to give their partner a thumbs-up if it is a mixed number and a thumbs-down if it is not.

- Say: *Whisper to your partner why you made that decision.* Discuss responses.

- Students are now ready for the **Mixed Number Fraction activities** on pages 8–9.

How to Play

- Each team chooses a colored token (tiles, cubes, chips).
- Each team tosses a die. Higher number goes first.
- Taking turns, teams toss a die or dice and follow the activity directions to arrive at a specific fraction.

FOUR-GRID TIC-TAC-TOE

- The object of the game is to place three tokens in a row on any of the four grids to win Tic-Tac-Toe.
- When no more plays are possible, the team with the most Tic-Tac-Toes wins.

FOUR IN A ROW

- The object of the game is to line up four tokens horizontally, vertically, or diagonally before the opposing team does.
  - The first team to line up 4 tokens wins.

CROSSOVER

- The object of the game is to place tokens so they form a continuous path zigzagging horizontally, vertically, or diagonally from one side of the chart to the other.
- A token may not be placed on an occupied space.
- The first team to form a continuous path across the chart wins.

Variations

- Start play in either the outside right or outside left column of the chart. If no square in either column contains the specific fraction needed, lose a turn.
- If the team that tosses first does place a token in a square in an outside column, the opposing team must place a token in a square in the opposite outside column.
- The first team to make a continuous path zigzagging horizontally, vertically, or diagonally from one side of the chart to the other (either top, bottom, left, or right) wins.

Differentiated Instruction

Activities can be differentiated to accommodate a variety of student learning abilities:

- Simplify activities by changing **Four in a Row** to **Three in a Row.**
- Increase challenge by limiting **Four in a Row** to either diagonal, horizontal, or vertical play.

Identifying Proper & Improper Fractions
Four-Grid Tic-Tac-Toe

How to Play

- Each team chooses a colored token.
- Teams toss a die. Higher number goes first.

- Toss a die. If the die toss is an **odd number,** place a marker on a **proper fraction** on any of the 4 grids.
- If the die toss is an **even number,** place a marker on an **improper fraction** on any of the 4 grids
- If a fraction is not available, lose that turn.
- The team with the most "threes in a row" wins.

$\dfrac{15}{14}$	$\dfrac{5}{2}$	$\dfrac{4}{8}$		$\dfrac{9}{10}$	$\dfrac{17}{18}$	$\dfrac{18}{17}$
$\dfrac{7}{8}$	$\dfrac{3}{1}$	$\dfrac{0}{3}$		$\dfrac{100}{99}$	$\dfrac{25}{13}$	$\dfrac{5}{10}$
$\dfrac{1}{2}$	$\dfrac{9}{4}$	$\dfrac{3}{4}$		$\dfrac{11}{6}$	$\dfrac{9}{12}$	$\dfrac{5}{7}$
$\dfrac{8}{7}$	$\dfrac{20}{10}$	$\dfrac{7}{16}$		$\dfrac{15}{16}$	$\dfrac{19}{17}$	$\dfrac{8}{3}$
$\dfrac{12}{6}$	$\dfrac{1}{9}$	$\dfrac{5}{6}$		$\dfrac{4}{11}$	$\dfrac{7}{14}$	$\dfrac{13}{12}$
$\dfrac{7}{6}$	$\dfrac{8}{12}$	$\dfrac{18}{9}$		$\dfrac{6}{12}$	$\dfrac{3}{6}$	$\dfrac{9}{2}$

Identifying Proper & Improper Fractions
Four in a Row/Crossover

How to Play

- Each team chooses a colored token.
- Teams toss a die. Higher number goes first.

- Choose a game: **Four in a Row** or **Crossover.**
- Toss a die. If the die toss is an **odd number,** place a marker on a **proper fraction.**
- If the die toss is an **even number,** place a marker on an **improper fraction.**
- If the fraction is not available, lose that turn.
- The first player to reach the goal of the game wins.

$\dfrac{1}{2}$	$\dfrac{4}{3}$	$\dfrac{2}{5}$	$\dfrac{6}{2}$	$\dfrac{8}{2}$
$\dfrac{5}{6}$	$\dfrac{2}{1}$	$\dfrac{3}{2}$	$\dfrac{8}{9}$	$\dfrac{1}{3}$
$\dfrac{6}{5}$	$\dfrac{2}{7}$	$\dfrac{7}{2}$	$\dfrac{4}{7}$	$\dfrac{5}{2}$
$\dfrac{5}{3}$	$\dfrac{11}{12}$	$\dfrac{8}{10}$	$\dfrac{10}{8}$	$\dfrac{4}{9}$
$\dfrac{1}{8}$	$\dfrac{7}{10}$	$\dfrac{8}{3}$	$\dfrac{7}{4}$	$\dfrac{1}{13}$

Identifying Improper & Mixed Fractions
Four-Grid Tic-Tac-Toe

How to Play

- Each team chooses a colored token.
- Teams toss a die. Higher number goes first.

- Toss a die. If the die toss is an **odd number**, place a marker on an **improper fraction** on any of the 4 grids.
- If the die toss is an **even number**, place a marker on a **mixed fraction** on any of the 4 grids.
- If a fraction is not available, lose that turn.
- The team with the most "threes in a row" wins.

$\frac{12}{11}$	$\frac{5}{3}$	$7\frac{5}{8}$		$3\frac{9}{10}$	$2\frac{1}{18}$	$\frac{18}{14}$
$2\frac{7}{8}$	$\frac{4}{3}$	$4\frac{1}{3}$		$\frac{100}{99}$	$\frac{25}{13}$	$7\frac{5}{10}$
$5\frac{1}{2}$	$\frac{8}{4}$	$1\frac{3}{4}$		$\frac{11}{6}$	$2\frac{5}{12}$	$\frac{15}{7}$
$\frac{9}{7}$	$\frac{20}{10}$	$2\frac{7}{8}$		$17\frac{3}{8}$	$\frac{19}{18}$	$13\frac{2}{3}$
$\frac{12}{6}$	$3\frac{6}{7}$	$6\frac{5}{9}$		$\frac{4}{1}$	$8\frac{1}{8}$	$\frac{13}{12}$
$\frac{7}{5}$	$9\frac{5}{9}$	$\frac{18}{9}$		$3\frac{2}{9}$	$7\frac{3}{5}$	$\frac{9}{1}$

How to Play

- Each team chooses a colored token.
- Teams toss a die. Higher number goes first.

- Choose a game: **Four in a Row** or **Crossover.**
- Toss a die. If the die toss is an **odd number,** place a marker on an **improper fraction.**
- If the die toss is an **even number,** place a marker on a **mixed fraction.**
- If the fraction is not available, lose that turn.
- The first player to reach the goal of the game wins.

$5\frac{1}{2}$	$\frac{4}{2}$	$4\frac{2}{5}$	$\frac{6}{1}$	$3\frac{2}{8}$
$\frac{6}{5}$	$7\frac{3}{4}$	$\frac{3}{2}$	$5\frac{8}{9}$	$9\frac{1}{3}$
$\frac{9}{6}$	$6\frac{2}{7}$	$\frac{7}{2}$	$\frac{8}{4}$	$5\frac{2}{9}$
$3\frac{6}{7}$	$\frac{11}{7}$	$4\frac{8}{10}$	$10\frac{1}{8}$	$\frac{9}{4}$
$\frac{8}{7}$	$2\frac{7}{10}$	$\frac{4}{3}$	$7\frac{2}{4}$	$\frac{13}{5}$

Finding Ones/Renaming Fractions Activities

Notes to Teachers – Finding Ones/Renaming Fractions

Objectives

- Students become familiar with creating fractions that equal 1.
- Students use the identity element 1 in the form of $\frac{1}{1}, \frac{2}{2}, \frac{3}{3}, \frac{4}{4}, \frac{5}{5}, \frac{6}{6}$ to create equivalent fractions for $\frac{1}{2}, \frac{1}{3}, \frac{1}{4}, \frac{1}{5}, \frac{1}{6}$.

Overview

The form $\frac{a \times n}{b \times n} = \frac{an}{bn}$ is the foundation for finding equivalent fractions and for multiplying fractions. Students engage in the **Finding Ones** and **Fraction Bar activities** to explore the role of the identity element for multiplication in finding equivalent fractions.

Getting Started

- Direct discussion questions (below) to teams of students, with two students per team.
- Allow time for each team to discuss their thinking and agree on a solution.
- In a large-group discussion, ask student teams to share their thinking.

Materials

Finding Ones

- 6 dice
- "Finding Ones" Score Chart (page 16)
- Fraction Bar Chart for teacher demonstration (page 120)
- Pencil

Renaming Fractions

- 6 dice
- "Renaming Fractions" score charts and fraction bar charts for halves, 3rds, 4ths, 5ths, or 6ths (pages 16–23)
- Pencil

LESSON 3: FRACTION NAMES FOR ONE (1)

- Display the fraction bar chart (page 120) using a document camera or sketch the chart on the board. Ask: *How is each row on this chart divided differently?*

- Direct students to whisper their response to their partner. Discuss responses.

- Through questioning, lead students to identify that each row is divided into a different number of equal sections.

- Ask: *How is each row the same?* (Through questioning, lead students to identify that the rows are all the same length.)

- Point to the row of thirds. Ask: *How many sectional parts are in this row?* (3) *Are they all equal?* (Yes.)

- Say: *Discuss with your partner and explain your thinking.*

- Ask: *If there are 3 sections in this row, what fraction name would you call one of the sections?* ($\frac{1}{3}$)

- Say: *Name the other sections in this row.* (Label each section $\frac{1}{3}$.)

LESSON 3: FRACTION NAMES FOR 1 (cont.)

- Ask: *What fraction name could you give to the whole fraction bar divided into 3 parts?* (Label the right side of the bar $\frac{3}{3}$.)

- Point to the first row on the fraction chart. Ask: *How many sections are in this row?* (1) *What fraction name would you give this bar?* (Label the bar $\frac{1}{1}$.)

- Give a copy of the fraction bar chart to each pair of students. Instruct student pairs to write a fraction name on each fraction section and a fraction name for the whole bar.

- Student pairs exchange their completed charts with another pair to check answers.

- Ask: *Which of these equations is true:* $\frac{4}{4} < \frac{6}{6}$, $\frac{4}{4} > \frac{6}{6}$, or $\frac{4}{4} = \frac{6}{6}$? ($\frac{4}{4} = \frac{6}{6}$)

- Say: *Explain your thinking to your partner.* Discuss class responses.

- Ask: *Is this a true statement?* $\frac{100}{100} = \frac{1000}{1000}$ (Yes.) *How can you prove it?*

- Ask (food for thought): *Is there an infinite number of fraction names for 1?* (Yes.)

- Students are now ready for the **Finding Ones** activity on pages 15–16.

- ## LESSON 4: ONE (1) AS THE IDENTITY ELEMENT IN MULTIPLICATION

- Pair students and give each pair a fraction bar chart (page 120). Write these equations on the board:

$$\frac{1}{1} \times 1 = 1 \qquad \frac{2}{2} \times 1 = 1 \qquad \frac{3}{3} \times 1 = 1 \qquad \frac{7}{7} \times 1 = ?$$

- Circle the fractions $\frac{1}{1}$, $\frac{2}{2}$, and $\frac{3}{3}$.

- Say: *Look at the circled fractions. Each fraction has different numbers, but how are they the same? Explain your thinking to your partner.*

- Ask: *If* $\frac{1}{1} \times 1 = 1$, $\frac{2}{2} \times 1 = 1$, *and* $\frac{3}{3} \times 1 = 1$, *what does* $\frac{7}{7} \times 1$ *equal?* Discuss responses.

- Ask: *What does* $4 \times \frac{7}{7}$ *equal?* (4) *What does* $\frac{100}{100} \times 4$ *equal?* (4) Discuss responses.

- Lead students to generalize that any whole number multiplied by 1 (or a fraction that equals 1) results in the same whole number. One (1) is called the **identity element for multiplication** because any number multiplied by 1 equals that same number.

- Write these 3 equations on the board: $\frac{1}{1} \times \frac{1}{3} = \frac{1}{3}$ $\qquad \frac{2}{2} \times \frac{1}{3} = \frac{2}{6}$ $\qquad \frac{3}{3} \times \frac{1}{3} = \frac{3}{9}$

- Point to $\frac{2}{6}$. Ask: *What numbers were multiplied that resulted in* $\frac{2}{6}$?

- Discuss class responses. Agree that $\frac{2 \times 1}{2 \times 3} = \frac{2}{6}$.

- Point to $\frac{3}{9}$. Ask: *What numbers were multiplied that resulted in* $\frac{3}{9}$?

- Discuss class responses. Agree that $\frac{3 \times 1}{3 \times 3} = \frac{3}{9}$.

- Direct student pairs to shade in $\frac{1}{3}$, $\frac{2}{6}$, and $\frac{3}{9}$ on their charts. Ask: *How are the shaded parts* $\frac{1}{3}$, $\frac{2}{6}$, *and* $\frac{3}{9}$ *the same? How are they different?* (continued, next page)

LESSON 4: ONE (1) AS THE IDENTITY ELEMENT IN MULTIPLICATION (cont.)

- Lead students to generalize that any fraction multiplied by a fraction name for 1 results in an equivalent fraction (a fraction equal in amount).

- Direct student pairs to look at their fraction bar charts for thirds (page 20). Say: *Look at the 4th row on the chart. Can you predict how many 12ths parts will be shaded in to equal $\frac{1}{3}$?* (Discuss with your partner and then shade in the parts.)

- Say: *Look at the 5th row on your chart. Can you predict how many 15ths parts will be shaded in to equal $\frac{1}{3}$?* (Discuss with your partner and then shade in the parts.)

- Say: *Look at the 6th row on the chart. Can you predict how many 18ths parts will be shaded in to equal $\frac{1}{3}$?* (Discuss with your partner and then shade in the parts.)

- Say: *Explain how this is true:* $\frac{1}{3} = \frac{2}{6} = \frac{3}{9} = \frac{4}{12} = \frac{5}{15} = \frac{6}{18}$.

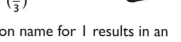

- Ask: *What would the fraction name for $\frac{1}{3}$ be for $\frac{7}{7} \times \frac{1}{3}$? $\frac{50}{50} \times \frac{1}{3}$? ($\frac{1}{3}$)*

- Lead students to generalize that any fraction multiplied by a fraction name for 1 results in an equivalent fraction (a fraction equal in amount).

- Ask (food for thought): *Are there an infinite number of fraction names for any fraction* (for example, $\frac{1}{3}, \frac{2}{6}, \frac{3}{9} \ldots$ to infinity)? (Yes.)

LESSON 4: IDENTITY ELEMENT FOR DIVISION

- Write these equations on the board:

  $8 \div 2 = 4$ and $\frac{8}{2} = 4$ $20 \div 4 = 5$ and $\frac{20}{4} = 5$ $100 \div 4 = 25$ and $\frac{100}{4} = 25$

- Say: *Discuss with your partner what you think the lines between these numbers mean.*

- Lead students to generalize that the lines mean division. Explain that when we see $\frac{8}{2}$, we can look at 8 fraction bars and count how many halves there are, or we can actually divide 8 by 2 (8 has how many 2s?). Say: *Which is the more efficent method? Discuss with your partner.*

- Write on the board: $4 \div 1 = 4$ $\frac{4}{1} = ?$ $\frac{7}{1} = ?$ $\frac{35}{1} = ?$

- Ask: *If 4 divided by 1 equals 4, what does $\frac{4}{1}$ equal? $\frac{7}{1}$? $\frac{35}{1}$?* Say: *Discuss with your partner and share your team's response with the class.*

- Ask: *What happens when any number is divided by 1?* (Discuss reponses.)

- Lead students to generalize that any whole number divided by 1 results in the original number. Say: *One (1) is also the identity element for division.*

- Ask each pair of students to create five fractions that show 1 as the identity element for division. (Students can use the back of the fraction bar chart to record these fractions.)

Students are now ready for the **Renaming Fractions** activities.

Equivalent Fractions – Finding Ones

How to Play

- Teams toss a die.
- Higher number goes first.
- Each team shares a score chart (page 16).

- Toss 6 dice.

- Find pairs of 2 dice that make a fraction that is equal to 1 (for example, $\frac{5}{5}$ and $\frac{1}{1}$).

- Shade in those fractions on the Finding Ones score chart.

- **Examples:**

    For the fraction $\frac{1}{1}$, shade in the fraction bar that has one section.

    For the fraction $\frac{5}{5}$, shade in the fraction bar that has 5 sections.

- After 5 tosses, the team with the most fraction bars shaded in wins that round.

- Play 2 or more rounds. The first team to win 2 rounds is the winner.

OR

- After 3 games, tally the 3 scores. The team with most fraction bars shaded in wins.

Finding Ones – Score Chart

Fraction Games & Activities with Dice!

Renaming Fractions – Fraction Bar Activities

How to Play

- Teams toss a die.
- Higher number goes first.
- Each team needs a chart.

- Toss 6 dice (for example, 2, 6, 3, 2, 1, 3).
- Look for pairs of 2 dice that make a fraction that equals 1.
  Example: 2 and 2 and 3 and 3.
- Record the pairs as fractions on the score chart in the row for Toss 1.
- Follow directions below for the chart you are using.

Renaming One-Half:

- Multiply each fraction that equals 1 by $\frac{1}{2}$.

- **Example:** $\dfrac{2 \times 1}{2 \times 2} = \dfrac{2}{4}$ $\dfrac{3 \times 1}{3 \times 2} = \dfrac{3}{6}$

  On the **Renaming One-Half** chart (page 19), find the fraction bar divided into 4ths. Shade in 2 of the 4ths. Find the fraction bar divided into 6ths. Shade in 3 of the 6ths. (Fraction bar sections can only be shaded in once.)

- Taking turns, each team tosses the 6 dice 5 times.

- If a team cannot shade in any fraction on their toss, the team loses a turn.

- The team with the most $\frac{1}{2}$ areas shaded in on the fraction bar chart wins that round.

- The first team to win 2 rounds wins. OR, the team with highest score after 3 rounds wins.

Renaming One-Third:

- Multiply each fraction that equals 1 by $\frac{1}{3}$.

- **Example:** $\dfrac{2 \times 1}{2 \times 3} = \dfrac{2}{6}$ $\dfrac{3 \times 1}{3 \times 3} = \dfrac{3}{9}$

  On the **Renaming One-Third** chart (page 20), find the fraction bar divided into 6ths. Shade in 2 of the 6ths. Find the fraction bar divided into 9ths. Shade in 3 of the 9ths. (Fraction bar sections can only be shaded in once.)

- Taking turns, each team tosses the 6 dice 5 times.

- If a team cannot shade in any fraction on their toss, the team loses a turn.

- The team with the most $\frac{1}{3}$ areas shaded in on the fraction bar chart wins that round.

- The first team to win 2 rounds wins. OR, the team with highest score after 3 rounds wins.

Renaming One-Fourth:

- Multiply each fraction that equals 1 by $\frac{1}{4}$.

- Example: $\dfrac{2 \times 1}{2 \times 4} = \dfrac{2}{8}$ $\dfrac{3 \times 1}{3 \times 4} = \dfrac{3}{12}$

  On the **Renaming One-Fourth** chart (page 21), find the fraction bar divided into 8ths. Shade in 2 of the 8ths. Find the fraction bar divided into 12ths. Shade in 3 of the 12ths. (Fraction bar sections can only be shaded in once.)

- Taking turns, each team tosses the 6 dice 5 times.

- If a team cannot shade in any fraction on their toss, the team loses a turn.

- The team with the most $\frac{1}{4}$ areas shaded in on the fraction bar chart wins that round.

- The first team to win 2 rounds wins. OR, the team with highest score after 3 rounds wins.

Renaming One-Fifth:

- Multiply each fraction that equals 1 by $\frac{1}{5}$.

- Example: $\dfrac{2 \times 1}{2 \times 5} = \dfrac{2}{10}$ $\dfrac{3 \times 1}{3 \times 5} = \dfrac{3}{15}$

  On the **Renaming One-Fifth** chart (page 22), find the fraction bar divided into 10ths. Shade in 2 of the 10ths. Find the fraction bar divided into 15ths. Shade in 3 of the 15ths. (Fraction bar sections can only be shaded in once.)

- Taking turns, each team tosses the 6 dice 5 times.

- If a team cannot shade in any fraction on their toss, the team loses a turn.

- The team with the most $\frac{1}{5}$ areas shaded in on the fraction bar chart wins that round.

- The first team to win 2 rounds wins. OR, the team with highest score after 3 rounds wins.

Renaming One-Sixth:

- Multiply each fraction that equals 1 by $\frac{1}{6}$.

- Example: $\dfrac{2 \times 1}{2 \times 6} = \dfrac{2}{12}$ $\dfrac{3 \times 1}{3 \times 6} = \dfrac{3}{18}$

  On the **Renaming One-Sixth** chart (page 23), find the fraction bar divided into 12ths. Shade in 2 of the 12ths. On the 6ths fraction bar chart, find the fraction bar divided into 18ths. Shade in 3 of the 18ths. (Fraction bar sections can only be shaded in once.)

- Taking turns, each team tosses the 6 dice 5 times.

- If a team cannot shade in any fraction on their toss, the team loses a turn.

- The team with the most $\frac{1}{6}$ areas shaded in on the fraction bar chart wins that round.

- The first team to win 2 rounds wins. OR, the team with highest score after 3 rounds wins.

Renaming One-Half – Fraction Bar Activity

Score Chart		
Rename fraction.	Rename fraction.	Rename fraction.
Toss 1 $\underline{\qquad} \times \dfrac{1}{2} =$	$\underline{\qquad} \times \dfrac{1}{2} =$	$\underline{\qquad} \times \dfrac{1}{2} =$
Toss 2 $\underline{\qquad} \times \dfrac{1}{2} =$	$\underline{\qquad} \times \dfrac{1}{2} =$	$\underline{\qquad} \times \dfrac{1}{2} =$
Toss 3 $\underline{\qquad} \times \dfrac{1}{2} =$	$\underline{\qquad} \times \dfrac{1}{2} =$	$\underline{\qquad} \times \dfrac{1}{2} =$
Toss 4 $\underline{\qquad} \times \dfrac{1}{2} =$	$\underline{\qquad} \times \dfrac{1}{2} =$	$\underline{\qquad} \times \dfrac{1}{2} =$
Toss 5 $\underline{\qquad} \times \dfrac{1}{2} =$	$\underline{\qquad} \times \dfrac{1}{2} =$	$\underline{\qquad} \times \dfrac{1}{2} =$

Renaming One-Half Chart: Shade in sections for each toss.

$\frac{1}{2}$				$\frac{1}{2}$			
$\frac{1}{4}$		$\frac{1}{4}$		$\frac{1}{4}$		$\frac{1}{4}$	
$\frac{1}{6}$		$\frac{1}{6}$		$\frac{1}{6}$	$\frac{1}{6}$		$\frac{1}{6}$	$\frac{1}{6}$
$\frac{1}{8}$	$\frac{1}{8}$	$\frac{1}{8}$	$\frac{1}{8}$	$\frac{1}{8}$	$\frac{1}{8}$	$\frac{1}{8}$	$\frac{1}{8}$
$\frac{1}{10}$	$\frac{1}{10}$	$\frac{1}{10}$	$\frac{1}{10}$	$\frac{1}{10}$	$\frac{1}{10}$	$\frac{1}{10}$	$\frac{1}{10}$	$\frac{1}{10}$	$\frac{1}{10}$
$\frac{1}{12}$	$\frac{1}{12}$	$\frac{1}{12}$	$\frac{1}{12}$	$\frac{1}{12}$	$\frac{1}{12}$	$\frac{1}{12}$	$\frac{1}{12}$	$\frac{1}{12}$	$\frac{1}{12}$	$\frac{1}{12}$	$\frac{1}{12}$

Renaming One-Third – Fraction Bar Activity

	Score Chart		
	Rename fraction.	Rename fraction.	Rename fraction.
Toss 1	—— × $\frac{1}{3}$ =	—— × $\frac{1}{3}$ =	—— × $\frac{1}{3}$ =
Toss 2	—— × $\frac{1}{3}$ =	—— × $\frac{1}{3}$ =	—— × $\frac{1}{3}$ =
Toss 3	—— × $\frac{1}{3}$ =	—— × $\frac{1}{3}$ =	—— × $\frac{1}{3}$ =
Toss 4	—— × $\frac{1}{3}$ =	—— × $\frac{1}{3}$ =	—— × $\frac{1}{3}$ =
Toss 5	—— × $\frac{1}{3}$ =	—— × $\frac{1}{3}$ =	—— × $\frac{1}{3}$ =

Renaming One-Third Chart: Shade in sections for each toss.

$\frac{1}{3}$				$\frac{1}{3}$				$\frac{1}{3}$			
$\frac{1}{6}$		$\frac{1}{6}$		$\frac{1}{6}$		$\frac{1}{6}$		$\frac{1}{6}$		$\frac{1}{6}$	
$\frac{1}{9}$		$\frac{1}{9}$	$\frac{1}{9}$	$\frac{1}{9}$		$\frac{1}{9}$	$\frac{1}{9}$	$\frac{1}{9}$	$\frac{1}{9}$		$\frac{1}{9}$
$\frac{1}{12}$	$\frac{1}{12}$	$\frac{1}{12}$	$\frac{1}{12}$	$\frac{1}{12}$	$\frac{1}{12}$	$\frac{1}{12}$	$\frac{1}{12}$	$\frac{1}{12}$	$\frac{1}{12}$	$\frac{1}{12}$	$\frac{1}{12}$
$\frac{1}{15}$	$\frac{1}{15}$	$\frac{1}{15}$	$\frac{1}{15}$	$\frac{1}{15}$	$\frac{1}{15}$	$\frac{1}{15}$	$\frac{1}{15}$	$\frac{1}{15}$	$\frac{1}{15}$	$\frac{1}{15}$	$\frac{1}{15}$	$\frac{1}{15}$	$\frac{1}{15}$	$\frac{1}{15}$
$\frac{1}{18}$	$\frac{1}{18}$	$\frac{1}{18}$	$\frac{1}{18}$	$\frac{1}{18}$	$\frac{1}{18}$	$\frac{1}{18}$	$\frac{1}{18}$	$\frac{1}{18}$	$\frac{1}{18}$	$\frac{1}{18}$	$\frac{1}{18}$	$\frac{1}{18}$	$\frac{1}{18}$	$\frac{1}{18}$	$\frac{1}{18}$	$\frac{1}{18}$	$\frac{1}{18}$

Renaming One-Fourth – Fraction Bar Activity

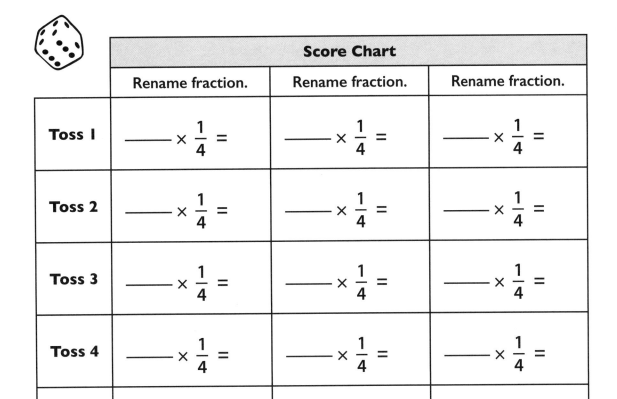

Score Chart		
Rename fraction.	Rename fraction.	Rename fraction.
Toss 1 ——— $\times \frac{1}{4}$ =	——— $\times \frac{1}{4}$ =	——— $\times \frac{1}{4}$ =
Toss 2 ——— $\times \frac{1}{4}$ =	——— $\times \frac{1}{4}$ =	——— $\times \frac{1}{4}$ =
Toss 3 ——— $\times \frac{1}{4}$ =	——— $\times \frac{1}{4}$ =	——— $\times \frac{1}{4}$ =
Toss 4 ——— $\times \frac{1}{4}$ =	——— $\times \frac{1}{4}$ =	——— $\times \frac{1}{4}$ =
Toss 5 ——— $\times \frac{1}{4}$ =	——— $\times \frac{1}{4}$ =	——— $\times \frac{1}{4}$ =

Renaming One-Fourth Chart: Shade in sections for each toss.

$\frac{1}{4}$		$\frac{1}{4}$		$\frac{1}{4}$		$\frac{1}{4}$	
$\frac{1}{8}$	$\frac{1}{8}$	$\frac{1}{8}$	$\frac{1}{8}$	$\frac{1}{8}$	$\frac{1}{8}$	$\frac{1}{8}$	$\frac{1}{8}$

(Fraction bar chart with rows of $\frac{1}{12}$, $\frac{1}{16}$, $\frac{1}{20}$, and $\frac{1}{24}$ sections)

Renaming One-Fifth – Fraction Bar Activity

Score Chart		
Rename fraction.	Rename fraction.	Rename fraction.
Toss 1 $\underline{\hspace{1cm}} \times \dfrac{1}{5} =$	$\underline{\hspace{1cm}} \times \dfrac{1}{5} =$	$\underline{\hspace{1cm}} \times \dfrac{1}{5} =$
Toss 2 $\underline{\hspace{1cm}} \times \dfrac{1}{5} =$	$\underline{\hspace{1cm}} \times \dfrac{1}{5} =$	$\underline{\hspace{1cm}} \times \dfrac{1}{5} =$
Toss 3 $\underline{\hspace{1cm}} \times \dfrac{1}{5} =$	$\underline{\hspace{1cm}} \times \dfrac{1}{5} =$	$\underline{\hspace{1cm}} \times \dfrac{1}{5} =$
Toss 4 $\underline{\hspace{1cm}} \times \dfrac{1}{5} =$	$\underline{\hspace{1cm}} \times \dfrac{1}{5} =$	$\underline{\hspace{1cm}} \times \dfrac{1}{5} =$
Toss 5 $\underline{\hspace{1cm}} \times \dfrac{1}{5} =$	$\underline{\hspace{1cm}} \times \dfrac{1}{5} =$	$\underline{\hspace{1cm}} \times \dfrac{1}{5} =$

Renaming One-Fifth Chart: Shade in sections for each toss.

$\dfrac{1}{5}$		$\dfrac{1}{5}$		$\dfrac{1}{5}$		$\dfrac{1}{5}$		$\dfrac{1}{5}$	
$\dfrac{1}{10}$	$\dfrac{1}{10}$	$\dfrac{1}{10}$	$\dfrac{1}{10}$	$\dfrac{1}{10}$	$\dfrac{1}{10}$	$\dfrac{1}{10}$	$\dfrac{1}{10}$	$\dfrac{1}{10}$	$\dfrac{1}{10}$

$\dfrac{1}{15}$ $\dfrac{1}{15}$ $\dfrac{1}{15}$ $\dfrac{1}{15}$ $\dfrac{1}{15}$ $\dfrac{1}{15}$ $\dfrac{1}{15}$ $\dfrac{1}{15}$ $\dfrac{1}{15}$ $\dfrac{1}{15}$ $\dfrac{1}{15}$ $\dfrac{1}{15}$ $\dfrac{1}{15}$ $\dfrac{1}{15}$ $\dfrac{1}{15}$

$\dfrac{1}{20}$ $\dfrac{1}{20}$ $\dfrac{1}{20}$ $\dfrac{1}{20}$ $\dfrac{1}{20}$ $\dfrac{1}{20}$ $\dfrac{1}{20}$ $\dfrac{1}{20}$ $\dfrac{1}{20}$ $\dfrac{1}{20}$ $\dfrac{1}{20}$ $\dfrac{1}{20}$ $\dfrac{1}{20}$ $\dfrac{1}{20}$ $\dfrac{1}{20}$ $\dfrac{1}{20}$ $\dfrac{1}{20}$ $\dfrac{1}{20}$ $\dfrac{1}{20}$ $\dfrac{1}{20}$

$\dfrac{1}{25}$ $\dfrac{1}{25}$

$\dfrac{1}{30}$ $\dfrac{1}{30}$

Renaming One-Sixth – Fraction Bar Activity

Score Chart		
Rename fraction.	Rename fraction.	Rename fraction.

	Rename fraction.	Rename fraction.	Rename fraction.
Toss 1	____ × $\frac{1}{6}$ =	____ × $\frac{1}{6}$ =	____ × $\frac{1}{6}$ =
Toss 2	____ × $\frac{1}{6}$ =	____ × $\frac{1}{6}$ =	____ × $\frac{1}{6}$ =
Toss 3	____ × $\frac{1}{6}$ =	____ × $\frac{1}{6}$ =	____ × $\frac{1}{6}$ =
Toss 4	____ × $\frac{1}{6}$ =	____ × $\frac{1}{6}$ =	____ × $\frac{1}{6}$ =
Toss 5	____ × $\frac{1}{6}$ =	____ × $\frac{1}{6}$ =	____ × $\frac{1}{6}$ =

Renaming One-Sixth Chart: Shade in sections for each toss.

$\frac{1}{6}$		$\frac{1}{6}$		$\frac{1}{6}$		$\frac{1}{6}$		$\frac{1}{6}$		$\frac{1}{6}$	
$\frac{1}{12}$	$\frac{1}{12}$	$\frac{1}{12}$	$\frac{1}{12}$	$\frac{1}{12}$	$\frac{1}{12}$	$\frac{1}{12}$	$\frac{1}{12}$	$\frac{1}{12}$	$\frac{1}{12}$	$\frac{1}{12}$	$\frac{1}{12}$

$\frac{1}{18}$ (×18)

$\frac{1}{24}$ (×24)

$\frac{1}{30}$ (×30)

$\frac{1}{36}$ (×36)

Renaming One-Half
Four-Grid Tic-Tac-Toe

- Each team chooses a colored token.
- Teams toss a die. Higher number goes first.

How to Play

- Toss a die. Make a fraction that equals 1. **Example:** Toss 3, make the fraction $\frac{3}{3}$.
- Multiply the fraction that equals 1 by $\frac{1}{2}$ to make an equivalent fraction for $\frac{1}{2}$. **Example:** $\frac{3 \times 1}{3 \times 2} = \frac{3}{6}$
- Place a marker on $\frac{3}{6}$ on any of the 4 Tic-Tac-Toe grids.
- If the fraction is not available, lose that turn.
- The team with the most "threes in a row" wins.

$\frac{2}{4}$	$\frac{5}{10}$	$\frac{4}{8}$		$\frac{1}{2}$	$\frac{6}{12}$	$\frac{3}{6}$
$\frac{4}{8}$	$\frac{1}{2}$	$\frac{3}{6}$		$\frac{6}{12}$	$\frac{4}{8}$	$\frac{5}{10}$
$\frac{3}{6}$	$\frac{2}{4}$	$\frac{6}{12}$		$\frac{5}{10}$	$\frac{2}{4}$	$\frac{1}{2}$
$\frac{1}{2}$	$\frac{3}{6}$	$\frac{4}{8}$		$\frac{5}{10}$	$\frac{6}{12}$	$\frac{2}{4}$
$\frac{6}{12}$	$\frac{5}{10}$	$\frac{1}{2}$		$\frac{2}{4}$	$\frac{3}{6}$	$\frac{4}{8}$
$\frac{2}{4}$	$\frac{4}{8}$	$\frac{3}{6}$		$\frac{6}{12}$	$\frac{5}{10}$	$\frac{1}{2}$

Renaming One-Half
Four in a Row/Crossover

- Each team chooses a colored token.
- Teams toss a die. Higher number goes first.

- Choose a game: **Four in a Row** or **Crossover.**
- Toss a die. Make a fraction that equals 1. Example: Toss 3, make the fraction $\frac{3}{3}$.
- Multiply the fraction that equals 1 by $\frac{1}{2}$ to make an equivalent fraction for $\frac{1}{2}$. **Example:** $\frac{3 \times 1}{3 \times 2} = \frac{3}{6}$
- Place a marker on $\frac{3}{6}$.
- If the fraction is not available, lose that turn.
- The first player to reach the goal of the game wins.

$\frac{2}{4}$	$\frac{4}{8}$	$\frac{5}{10}$	$\frac{3}{6}$	$\frac{6}{12}$
$\frac{5}{10}$	$\frac{1}{2}$	$\frac{3}{6}$	$\frac{6}{12}$	$\frac{4}{8}$
$\frac{1}{2}$	$\frac{3}{6}$	$\frac{6}{12}$	$\frac{5}{10}$	$\frac{2}{4}$
$\frac{5}{10}$	$\frac{2}{4}$	$\frac{4}{8}$	$\frac{3}{6}$	$\frac{1}{2}$
$\frac{3}{6}$	$\frac{6}{12}$	$\frac{1}{2}$	$\frac{2}{4}$	$\frac{4}{8}$

Fraction Games & Activities with Dice!

Renaming One-Third
Four-Grid Tic-Tac-Toe

- Each team chooses a colored token.
- Teams toss a die. Higher number goes first.

How to Play

- Toss a die. Make a fraction that equals 1. **Example:** Toss 3, make the fraction $\frac{3}{3}$.
- Multiply the fraction that equals 1 by $\frac{1}{3}$ to make an equivalent fraction for $\frac{1}{3}$. **Example:** $\frac{3 \times 1}{3 \times 3} = \frac{3}{9}$
- Place a marker on $\frac{3}{9}$ on any of the 4 Tic-Tac-Toe grids.
- If the fraction is not available, lose that turn.
- The team with the most "threes in a row" wins.

$\frac{1}{3}$	$\frac{5}{15}$	$\frac{3}{9}$		$\frac{6}{18}$	$\frac{4}{12}$	$\frac{2}{6}$
$\frac{3}{9}$	$\frac{6}{18}$	$\frac{2}{6}$		$\frac{4}{12}$	$\frac{3}{9}$	$\frac{5}{15}$
$\frac{2}{6}$	$\frac{1}{3}$	$\frac{4}{12}$		$\frac{5}{15}$	$\frac{1}{3}$	$\frac{6}{18}$
$\frac{6}{18}$	$\frac{2}{6}$	$\frac{3}{9}$		$\frac{5}{15}$	$\frac{4}{12}$	$\frac{1}{3}$
$\frac{4}{12}$	$\frac{5}{15}$	$\frac{6}{18}$		$\frac{1}{3}$	$\frac{2}{6}$	$\frac{3}{9}$
$\frac{1}{3}$	$\frac{3}{9}$	$\frac{2}{6}$		$\frac{4}{12}$	$\frac{5}{15}$	$\frac{6}{18}$

Renaming One-Third
Four in a Row/Crossover

How to Play

- Each team chooses a colored token.
- Teams toss a die. Higher number goes first.

- Choose a game: **Four in a Row** or **Crossover.**
- Toss a die. Make a fraction that equals 1. **Example:** Toss 3, make the fraction $\frac{3}{3}$.
- Multiply the fraction that equals 1 by $\frac{1}{3}$ to make an equivalent fraction for $\frac{1}{3}$. **Example:** $\frac{3 \times 1}{3 \times 3} = \frac{3}{9}$
- Place a marker on $\frac{3}{9}$.
- If the fraction is not available, lose that turn.
- The first player to reach the goal of the game wins.

$\frac{1}{3}$	$\frac{4}{12}$	$\frac{5}{15}$	$\frac{2}{6}$	$\frac{6}{18}$
$\frac{5}{15}$	$\frac{3}{9}$	$\frac{2}{6}$	$\frac{6}{18}$	$\frac{4}{12}$
$\frac{3}{9}$	$\frac{2}{6}$	$\frac{6}{18}$	$\frac{5}{15}$	$\frac{1}{3}$
$\frac{5}{15}$	$\frac{1}{3}$	$\frac{4}{12}$	$\frac{2}{6}$	$\frac{3}{9}$
$\frac{2}{6}$	$\frac{6}{18}$	$\frac{3}{9}$	$\frac{1}{3}$	$\frac{4}{12}$

Renaming One-Fourth
Four-Grid Tic-Tac-Toe

- Each team chooses a colored token.
- Teams toss a die. Higher number goes first.

How to Play

- Toss a die. Make a fraction that equals 1. **Example:** Toss 3, make the fraction $\frac{3}{3}$.
- Multiply the fraction that equals 1 by $\frac{1}{4}$ to make an equivalent fraction for $\frac{1}{4}$. **Example:** $\frac{3 \times 1}{3 \times 4} = \frac{3}{12}$
- Place a marker on $\frac{3}{12}$ on any of the 4 Tic-Tac-Toe grids.
- If the fraction is not available, lose that turn.
- The team with the most "threes in a row" wins.

$\frac{6}{24}$	$\frac{5}{20}$	$\frac{1}{4}$		$\frac{4}{16}$	$\frac{3}{12}$	$\frac{2}{8}$
$\frac{1}{4}$	$\frac{4}{16}$	$\frac{2}{8}$		$\frac{3}{12}$	$\frac{1}{4}$	$\frac{5}{20}$
$\frac{2}{8}$	$\frac{6}{24}$	$\frac{3}{12}$		$\frac{5}{20}$	$\frac{6}{24}$	$\frac{4}{16}$
$\frac{4}{16}$	$\frac{2}{8}$	$\frac{1}{4}$		$\frac{5}{20}$	$\frac{3}{12}$	$\frac{6}{24}$
$\frac{3}{12}$	$\frac{5}{20}$	$\frac{4}{16}$		$\frac{6}{24}$	$\frac{2}{8}$	$\frac{1}{4}$
$\frac{6}{24}$	$\frac{1}{4}$	$\frac{2}{8}$		$\frac{3}{12}$	$\frac{5}{20}$	$\frac{4}{16}$

Renaming One-Fourth
Four in a Row/Crossover

How to Play

- Each team chooses a colored token.
- Teams toss a die. Higher number goes first.

- Choose a game: **Four in a Row** or **Crossover.**
- Toss a die. Make a fraction that equals 1. **Example:** Toss 3, make the fraction $\frac{3}{3}$.
- Multiply the fraction that equals 1 by $\frac{1}{4}$ to make an equivalent fraction for $\frac{1}{4}$. **Example:** $\frac{3 \times 1}{3 \times 4} = \frac{3}{12}$
- Place a marker on $\frac{3}{12}$ on any of the 4 Tic-Tac-Toe grids.
- If the fraction is not available, lose that turn.
- The first player to reach the goal of the game wins.

$\frac{4}{16}$	$\frac{3}{12}$	$\frac{1}{4}$	$\frac{6}{24}$	$\frac{2}{8}$
$\frac{1}{4}$	$\frac{5}{20}$	$\frac{6}{24}$	$\frac{2}{8}$	$\frac{3}{12}$
$\frac{5}{20}$	$\frac{6}{24}$	$\frac{2}{8}$	$\frac{1}{4}$	$\frac{4}{16}$
$\frac{1}{4}$	$\frac{4}{16}$	$\frac{3}{12}$	$\frac{6}{24}$	$\frac{5}{20}$
$\frac{6}{24}$	$\frac{2}{8}$	$\frac{5}{20}$	$\frac{4}{16}$	$\frac{3}{12}$

Renaming One-Fifth
Four-Grid Tic-Tac-Toe

- Each team chooses a colored token.
- Teams toss a die. Higher number goes first.

How to Play

- Toss a die. Make a fraction that equals 1. **Example:** Toss 3, make the fraction $\frac{3}{3}$.
- Multiply the fraction that equals 1 by $\frac{1}{5}$ to make an equivalent fraction for $\frac{1}{5}$. **Example:** $\frac{3 \times 1}{3 \times 5} = \frac{3}{15}$
- Place a marker on $\frac{3}{15}$ on any of the 4 Tic-Tac-Toe grids.
- If the fraction is not available, lose that turn.
- The team with the most "threes in a row" wins.

$\frac{5}{25}$	$\frac{4}{20}$	$\frac{2}{10}$		$\frac{1}{5}$	$\frac{3}{15}$	$\frac{6}{30}$
$\frac{2}{10}$	$\frac{1}{5}$	$\frac{6}{30}$		$\frac{3}{15}$	$\frac{2}{10}$	$\frac{4}{20}$
$\frac{6}{30}$	$\frac{5}{25}$	$\frac{3}{15}$		$\frac{4}{20}$	$\frac{5}{25}$	$\frac{1}{5}$
$\frac{1}{5}$	$\frac{6}{30}$	$\frac{2}{10}$		$\frac{4}{20}$	$\frac{3}{15}$	$\frac{5}{25}$
$\frac{3}{15}$	$\frac{4}{20}$	$\frac{1}{5}$		$\frac{5}{25}$	$\frac{6}{30}$	$\frac{2}{10}$
$\frac{5}{25}$	$\frac{2}{10}$	$\frac{6}{30}$		$\frac{3}{15}$	$\frac{4}{20}$	$\frac{1}{5}$

Renaming One-Fifth
Four in a Row/Crossover

How to Play

- Each team chooses a colored token.
- Teams toss a die. Higher number goes first.

- Choose a game: **Four in a Row** or **Crossover.**
- Toss a die. Make a fraction that equals 1. **Example:** Toss 3, make the fraction $\frac{3}{3}$.
- Multiply the fraction that equals 1 by $\frac{1}{5}$ to make an equivalent fraction for $\frac{1}{5}$. **Example:** $\frac{3 \times 1}{3 \times 5} = \frac{3}{15}$.
- Place a marker on $\frac{3}{15}$.
- If the fraction is not available, lose that turn.
- The first player to reach the goal of the game wins.

$\frac{5}{25}$	$\frac{3}{15}$	$\frac{2}{10}$	$\frac{4}{20}$	$\frac{1}{5}$
$\frac{2}{10}$	$\frac{6}{30}$	$\frac{4}{20}$	$\frac{1}{5}$	$\frac{3}{15}$
$\frac{6}{30}$	$\frac{4}{20}$	$\frac{1}{5}$	$\frac{2}{10}$	$\frac{5}{25}$
$\frac{2}{10}$	$\frac{5}{25}$	$\frac{3}{15}$	$\frac{4}{20}$	$\frac{6}{30}$
$\frac{4}{20}$	$\frac{1}{5}$	$\frac{6}{30}$	$\frac{5}{25}$	$\frac{3}{15}$

Renaming One-Sixth
Four-Grid Tic-Tac-Toe

- Each team chooses a colored token.
- Teams toss a die. Higher number goes first.

How to Play

- Toss a die. Make a fraction that equals 1. **Example:** Toss 3, make the fraction $\frac{3}{3}$.

- Multiply the fraction that equals 1 by $\frac{1}{6}$ to make an equivalent fraction for $\frac{1}{6}$. **Example:** $\frac{3 \times 1}{3 \times 6} = \frac{3}{18}$.

- Place a marker on $\frac{3}{18}$ on any of the 4 Tic-Tac-Toe grids.

- If the fraction is not available, lose that turn.

- The team with the most "threes in a row" wins.

$\frac{4}{24}$	$\frac{5}{30}$	$\frac{6}{36}$		$\frac{1}{6}$	$\frac{2}{12}$	$\frac{3}{18}$
$\frac{6}{36}$	$\frac{1}{6}$	$\frac{3}{18}$		$\frac{2}{12}$	$\frac{6}{36}$	$\frac{5}{30}$
$\frac{3}{18}$	$\frac{4}{24}$	$\frac{2}{12}$		$\frac{5}{30}$	$\frac{4}{24}$	$\frac{1}{6}$
$\frac{1}{6}$	$\frac{3}{18}$	$\frac{6}{36}$		$\frac{5}{30}$	$\frac{2}{12}$	$\frac{4}{24}$
$\frac{2}{12}$	$\frac{5}{30}$	$\frac{1}{6}$		$\frac{4}{24}$	$\frac{3}{18}$	$\frac{6}{36}$
$\frac{4}{24}$	$\frac{6}{36}$	$\frac{3}{18}$		$\frac{2}{12}$	$\frac{5}{30}$	$\frac{1}{6}$

Renaming One-Sixth
Four in a Row/Crossover

How to Play

- Each team chooses a colored token.
- Teams toss a die. Higher number goes first.

- Choose a game: **Four in a Row** or **Crossover**.
- Toss a die. Make a fraction that equals 1. **Example:** Toss 3, make the fraction $\frac{3}{3}$.
- Multiply the fraction that equals 1 by $\frac{1}{6}$ to make an equivalent fraction for $\frac{1}{6}$. **Example:** $\frac{3 \times 1}{3 \times 6} = \frac{3}{18}$.
- Place a marker on $\frac{3}{18}$.
- If the fraction is not available, lose that turn.
- The first player to reach the goal of the game wins.

$\frac{1}{6}$	$\frac{6}{36}$	$\frac{2}{12}$	$\frac{5}{30}$	$\frac{4}{24}$
$\frac{2}{12}$	$\frac{3}{18}$	$\frac{5}{30}$	$\frac{4}{24}$	$\frac{6}{36}$
$\frac{3}{18}$	$\frac{5}{30}$	$\frac{4}{24}$	$\frac{2}{12}$	$\frac{1}{6}$
$\frac{2}{12}$	$\frac{1}{6}$	$\frac{6}{36}$	$\frac{5}{30}$	$\frac{3}{18}$
$\frac{5}{30}$	$\frac{4}{24}$	$\frac{3}{18}$	$\frac{1}{6}$	$\frac{6}{36}$

Fraction Bar Activities

Contents

Notes to Teachers/Fraction Bar Activities

- Using fraction bars as a visual model, students conceptually add/multiply (repeated addition), subtract, and divide (has how many) fractions.
- Students develop the concept of a whole equaling the sum of its equal parts, focusing on halves, thirds, fourths, fifths, and sixths.

Overview

Using fraction bars as a visual model, students toss a die to add/multiply, subtract, and divide fractional parts. They record their scores on a chart. Depending on the activity, the team with the highest or lowest score wins. Students are introduced to the concept of division through the term "has how many," focusing on whole fraction bars to determine how many fractional parts there are in each bar.

Getting Started

- Direct discussion questions (below) to teams of students, with two students per team.
- Allow time for each team to discuss their thinking and agree on a solution.
- In a large-group discussion, ask student teams to share their thinking.
- Ask for different ways of arriving at their conclusions, if there were any.

LESSON 5: USING FRACTION BARS TO ADD/MULTIPLY FRACTIONAL PARTS

- Display the fraction bar chart for halves (page 39).
- Ask: *If I shade in 4 halves, how many whole bars have I shaded in?* (2) Say: *Discuss with your partner and explain your thinking.*
- Discuss class responses. Write on the board: $\frac{1}{2} + \frac{1}{2} + \frac{1}{2} + \frac{1}{2} = 2$.
- Say: *Another way of saying "a half plus a half plus a half plus a half" is "4 of the halves." Another way of writing this is to* **use the multiplication symbol, ×, for "of the"**: $4 \times \frac{1}{2} = 2$.
- Ask: *If I shade in 3 of the halves, how many whole bars are shaded in?* (1) *Is there any part of another whole bar that is shaded in?* ($\frac{1}{2}$)
- Say: *Discuss with your partner and explain your thinking.* Discuss class responses.
- Say: *A half plus a half plus a half equals one and a half.* Write on the board: $\frac{1}{2} + \frac{1}{2} + \frac{1}{2} = 1\frac{1}{2}$.
- Say: *Three of the halves equal one and a half.* Write on the board: $3 \times \frac{1}{2} = 1\frac{1}{2}$.
- Use a similar introduction for adding/multiplying fourths, fifths, and sixths.

Students are now ready for the **Adding/Multiplying Fraction Bar** activities.

LESSON 6: USING FRACTION BARS TO SUBTRACT FRACTIONAL PARTS

- Display the fraction bar chart for halves (page 45).
- Ask: *If I start with two whole bars (circle 2 whole bars) and remove one of the halves (cross out one of the halves), what is left?* ($1\frac{1}{2}$)
- Say: *Discuss with your partner and explain your thinking.* Discuss class responses.
- Say: *Two minus a half equals one and a half.* Write the equation on the board: $2 - \frac{1}{2} = 1\frac{1}{2}$.
- Ask: *If I start with three whole bars and remove one and a half bars, what do I have left?* (Circle 3 bars and cross out $1\frac{1}{2}$ bars.)
- Say: *Discuss with your partner and explain your thinking.* Discuss class responses.
- Say: *Three minus one and a half equals one and a half.* Write the equation on the board: $3 - 1\frac{1}{2} = 1\frac{1}{2}$.
- Use a similar introduction for subtraction with thirds, fourths, fifths, and sixths.

Students are now ready for the **Subtracting Fraction Bar** activities.

LESSON 7: USING FRACTION BARS TO DIVIDE FRACTIONAL PARTS

- Display the fraction bar chart for halves (page 51).
- Ask: *If I start with two whole bars divided into halves (circle two whole bars), how many halves are there altogether? Here's another way to think about this: Two whole bars* **has how many** *halves?* (4)
- Write the equation on the board: $2 \div \frac{1}{2} = ?$ Say: *We read the division sign as "has how many."*
- Say: *Discuss with your partner and explain your thinking.* Discuss class responses.
- Say: *So two whole bars have four halves:* $2 \div \frac{1}{2} = 4$.
- Ask: *If I start with four whole bars divided into halves (circle four whole bars), how many halves are there in four wholes? Or four* **has how many** *halves?* $4 \div \frac{1}{2} = ?$ (8)
- Say: *Discuss with your partner and explain your thinking.* Discuss class responses.
- Ask: *Six has how many halves? Make a prediction.* (12)
- Say: *Discuss your answer with your partner.*
- Use a similar introduction for division with thirds, fourths, fifths, and sixths.

Students are now ready for the **Division (Has How Many) Fraction Bar** activities.

Adding/Multiplying Fractional Parts – Score Chart

Die Toss	Fraction	Proper or Mixed Fraction	Score
	Total – Game 1		

Die Toss	Fraction	Proper or Mixed Fraction	Score
	Total – Game 2		

Die Toss	Fraction	Proper or Mixed Fraction	Score
	Total – Game 3		

	Score
Game 1	
Game 2	
Game 3	
Total Score	

Fraction Bars – Adding/Multiplying Halves

- Each team gets a score chart, bar chart, die, and pencil.

- Toss a die.

- Make a fraction: Numerator = die toss, denominator = 2. (**Example:** Toss 5. Make the fraction $\frac{5}{2}$. Five-halves is $\frac{1}{2} + \frac{1}{2} + \frac{1}{2} + \frac{1}{2} + \frac{1}{2}$, or 5 of the halves.)

- Cross out that many halves on the fraction bar chart.

- On the score chart, record the die toss, the fraction created by the die toss, and the score.

- After 5 tosses, the teams total their scores. The team with the highest score wins.

- Play 2 or more games. First team to win 2 games is the winner.

Fraction Bars – Adding/Multiplying Thirds

- Each team gets a score chart (page 38), bar chart, die, and pencil.

- Toss a die.

- Make a fraction: Numerator = die toss, denominator = 3. (**Example:** Toss 5. Make the fraction $\frac{5}{3}$. Five-thirds is $\frac{1}{3}$ + $\frac{1}{3}$ + $\frac{1}{3}$ + $\frac{1}{3}$ + $\frac{1}{3}$, or 5 of the thirds.)

- Cross out that many thirds on the fraction bar chart.

- On the score chart, record the die toss, the fraction created by the die toss, and the score.

- After 5 tosses, the teams total their scores. The team with the highest score wins.

- Play 2 or more games. First team to win 2 games is the winner.

Fraction Bars – Adding/Multiplying Fourths

How to Play

- Each team gets a score chart (page 38), bar chart, die, and pencil.

- Toss a die.

- Make a fraction: Numerator = die toss, denominator = 4. (**Example:** Toss 5. Make the fraction $\frac{5}{4}$. Five-fourths is $\frac{1}{4}$ + $\frac{1}{4}$ + $\frac{1}{4}$ + $\frac{1}{4}$ + $\frac{1}{4}$, or 5 of the fourths.)

- Cross out that many fourths on the fraction bar chart.

- On the score chart, record the die toss, the fraction created by the die toss, and the score.

- After 5 tosses, the teams total their scores. The team with the highest score wins.

- Play 2 or more games. First team to win 2 games is the winner.

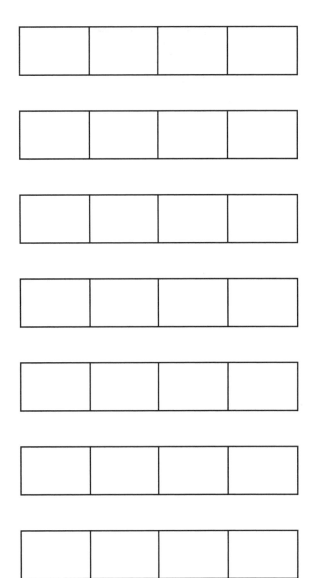

Fraction Games & Activities with Dice!

Fraction Bars – Adding/Multiplying Fifths

- Each team gets a score chart (page 38), bar chart, die, and pencil.
- Toss a die.
- Make a fraction: Numerator = die toss, denominator = 5. (**Example:** Toss 4. Make the fraction $\frac{4}{5}$. Four-fifths is $\frac{1}{5} + \frac{1}{5} + \frac{1}{5} + \frac{1}{5}$, or 4 of the fifths.)
- Cross out that many fifths on the fraction bar chart.
- On the score chart, record the die toss, the fraction created by the die toss, and the score.
- After 5 tosses, the teams total their scores. The team with the highest score wins.
- Play 2 or more games. First team to win 2 games is the winner.

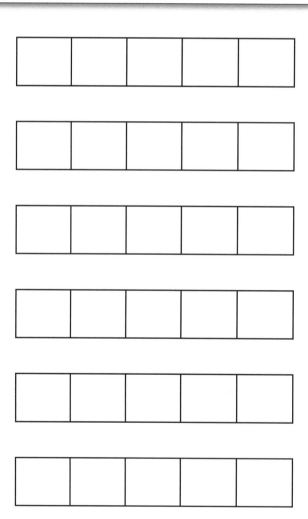

Fraction Bars – Adding/Multiplying Sixths

How to Play

- Each team gets a score chart (page 38), bar chart, die, and pencil.

- Toss a die.

- Make a fraction: Numerator = die toss, denominator = 6. (**Example:** Toss 4. Make the fraction $\frac{4}{6}$. Four-sixths is $\frac{1}{6} + \frac{1}{6} + \frac{1}{6} + \frac{1}{6}$, or 4 of the sixths.)

- Cross out that many sixths on the fraction bar chart.

- On the score chart, record the die toss, the fraction created by the die toss, and the score.

- After 5 tosses, the teams total their scores. The team with the highest score wins.

- Play 2 or more games. First team to win 2 games is the winner.

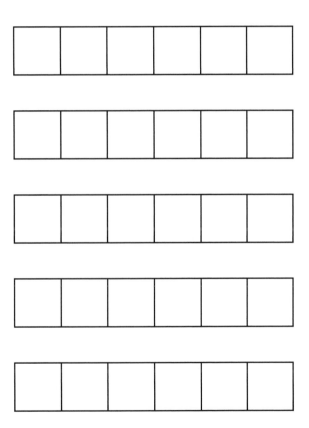

Subtracting Fractional Parts – Score Chart

Die Toss	Fraction	How many parts are left?

Die Toss	Fraction	How many parts are left?

Die Toss	Fraction	How many parts are left?

	Score
Game 1	
Game 2	
Game 3	
Total Score	

Fraction Bars – Subtracting Halves

- Each team gets a score chart (page 44), bar chart, die, and pencil.
- Toss a die.
- Make a fraction: Numerator = die toss, denominator = **2.**
- Starting from the **bar on the bottom right**, **cross out** that many **halves. (Example:** Toss 5. Make the fraction $\frac{5}{2}$. Cross out five halves.)
- On the score chart, record the die toss, the fraction created by the die toss, and how many fractional parts remain that are not crossed out.
- After 5 tosses, the team with the fewest halves crossed out wins.
- Play 2 or more games. First team to win 2 games is the winner.

Fraction Bars – Subtracting Thirds

How to Play

- Each team gets a score chart (page 44), bar chart, die, and pencil.

- Toss a die.

- Make a fraction: Numerator = die toss, denominator = **3.**

- Starting from the **bottom bar, cross out** that many **thirds. (Example:** Toss 4. Make the fraction $\frac{4}{3}$. Cross out four thirds.)

- On the score chart, record the die toss, the fraction created by the die toss, and how many fractional parts remain that are not crossed out.

- After 5 tosses, the team with the fewest thirds crossed out wins.

- Play 2 or more games. First team to win 2 games is the winner.

Fraction Bars – Subtracting Fourths

How to Play

- Each team gets a score chart (page 44), bar chart, die, and pencil.

- Toss a die.

- Make a fraction: Numerator = die toss, denominator = **4.**

- Starting from the **bottom bar, cross out** that many **fourths. (Example:** Toss 6. Make the fraction $\frac{6}{4}$. Cross out six fourths.)

- On the score chart, record the die toss, the fraction created by the die toss, and how many fractional parts remain that are not crossed out.

- After 5 tosses, the team with the fewest fourths crossed out wins.

- Play 2 or more games. First team to win 2 games is the winner.

Fraction Bars – Subtracting Fifths

- Each team gets a score chart (page 44), bar chart, die, and pencil.
- Toss a die.
- Make a fraction: Numerator = die toss, denominator = **5.**
- Starting from the **bottom bar, cross out** that many **fifths. (Example:** Toss 6. Make the fraction $\frac{6}{5}$. Cross out six fifths.)
- On the score chart, record the die toss, the fraction created by the die toss, and how many fractional parts remain that are not crossed out.
- After 5 tosses, the team with the fewest fifths crossed out wins.
- Play 2 or more games. First team to win 2 games is the winner.

Fraction Bars – Subtracting Sixths

- Each team gets a score chart (page 44), bar chart, die, and pencil.

- Toss a die.

- Make a fraction: Numerator = die toss, denominator = **6.**

- Starting from the **bottom cross out** that many **sixths. (Example:** Toss 4. Make the fraction $\frac{4}{6}$. Cross out four sixths.)

- On the score chart, record the die toss, the fraction created by the die toss, and how many fractional parts remain that are not crossed out.

- After 5 tosses, the team with the fewest sixths crossed out wins.

- Play 2 or more games. First team to win 2 games is the winner.

"Has How Many" Fractional Parts (Division) – Score Chart

Toss	Fractional parts in toss	Score
Total – Game 1		

Toss	Fractional parts in toss	Score
Total – Game 2		

Toss	Fractional parts in toss	Score
Total – Game 3		

	Score
Game 1	
Game 2	
Game 3	
Total	

Fraction Bars – "Has How Many" Halves
(Division)

- Each team gets a score chart (page 50), bar chart, die, and pencil.
- Toss a die. Each dot = a whole bar.
- Use the fraction bar chart to find out how many halves in the die toss number.
  (**Example:** Toss 3. Three whole fraction bars have how many halves? Three bars have 6 halves. Your score is 6.)
- On the score chart, record the die toss, the fraction created by the die toss, and the score.
- After 5 tosses, the teams total their scores. The team with the highest score wins.
- Play 2 or more games. The first team to win 2 games is the winner.

Fraction Bars – "Has How Many" Thirds
(Division)

How to Play

- Each team gets a score chart (page 50), bar chart, die, and pencil.

- Toss a die. Each dot = a whole bar.

- Use the fraction bar chart to find out how many thirds in the die toss number. (**Example:** Toss 3. Three whole fraction bars have how many thirds? Three bars have 9 thirds. Your score is 9.)

- On the score chart, record the die toss, the number of thirds, and the score.

- After 5 tosses, the teams total their scores. The team with the highest score wins.

- Play 2 or more games. The first team to win 2 games is the winner.

Fraction Bars – "Has How Many" Fourths
(Division)

How to Play

- Each team gets a score chart (page 50), bar chart, die, and pencil.
- Toss a die. Each dot = a whole bar.
- Use the fraction bar chart to find out how many fourths in the die toss number. (**Example:** Toss 3. Three whole fraction bars have how many fourths? Three bars have 12 fourths. Your score is 12.)
- On the score chart, record the die toss, the number of fourths, and the score.
- After 5 tosses, the teams total their scores. The team with the highest score wins.
- Play 2 or more games. The first team to win 2 games is the winner.

Fraction Bars – "Has How Many" Fifths
(Division)

- Each team gets a score chart (page 50), bar chart, die, and pencil.

- Toss a die. Each dot = a whole bar.

- Use the fraction bar chart to find out how many fifths in the die toss number.
  (**Example:** Toss 3. Three whole fraction bars have how many fifths?
  Three bars have 15 fifths. Your score is 15.)

- On the score chart, record the die toss, the number of fifths, and the score.

- After 5 tosses, the teams total their scores. The team with the highest score wins.

- Play 2 or more games. The first team to win 2 games is the winner.

Fraction Bars – "Has How Many" Sixths
(Division)

How to Play

- Each team gets a score chart (page 50), bar chart, die, and pencil.

- Toss a die. Each dot = a whole bar.

- Use the fraction bar chart to find out how many sixths in the die toss number.
  (**Example:** Toss 3. Three whole fraction bars have how many sixths?
  Three bars have 18 sixths. Your score is 18.)

- On the score chart, record the die toss, the number of sixths, and the score.

- After 5 tosses, the teams total their scores. The team with the highest score wins.

- Play 2 or more games. The first team to win 2 games is the winner.

Fraction Games & Activities with Dice!

Fraction Number Line Activities

Contents

Notes to Teachers/Fraction Number Line Activities

Objectives

- Students recognize fractions in a linear format, specifically, the number line.
- Students develop the concept of a whole equaling the sum of its equal parts, focusing on halves, thirds, fourths, fifths, and sixths.

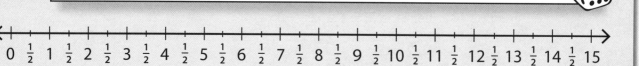

Overview

The Fraction Number Line activities are similar to the **Fraction Bar activities;** however, the model used is a linear or horizontal visual cue, the number line.

Student teams toss a die to add/multiply, subtract, and divide fractional parts on a number line and record their running scores on a chart. Each team has 5 tosses. The team that scores closest to a specified number wins.

Again, students are exposed to the concept of division through the term "has how many,"

meaning that students determine how many fractional parts make up each whole number on the number line.

Getting Started

Direct questions to student teams (pairs). Allow time for the teams to discuss their thinking and agree on a solution. In a large-group discussion, ask student teams to share their thinking with one another. Ask for different ways of arriving at their conclusions, if any.

LESSON 8: USING A NUMBER LINE TO ADD/MULTIPLY FRACTIONAL PARTS

- Copy the halves number line on the board (page 61) or display with a document camera. Each team should have their own copy of page 61.

- Say: *Start at 0 on the number line and count off 4 of the halves. Mark this point on your number line with your partner.*

- Have a student team demonstrate on the board how they counted the 4 halves.

- Write on the board: $\frac{1}{2} + \frac{1}{2} + \frac{1}{2} + \frac{1}{2} = 2$.

- Say: *Another way of writing this equation is to use the symbol × for "of the":* $4 \times \frac{1}{2} = 2$.

- Repeat these questions with different amounts, such as 7 halves, 12 halves. Write on the board the numerical representations: $7 \times \frac{1}{2} = ?$ $\left(\frac{7}{2}\right)$; $12 \times \frac{1}{2} = ?$ (6)

- Use the number lines provided for each activity (pages 62–65) to introduce adding/multiplying thirds, fourths, fifths, and sixths.

Students are now ready for the **Fraction Number Line activities for Addition/ Multiplication.**

LESSON 9: USING A NUMBER LINE TO SUBTRACT FRACTIONAL PARTS

- Copy the halves number line on the board (page 66) or display with a document camera. Each team should have their own copy of page 66.

- Say: *Start at 5 on the number line. Remove 3 halves. Mark this point on your number line. Where did you end up?*

- Have a student team demonstrate on the board how they determined the number of halves.

- Write on the board: $5 - \frac{3}{2} = 3\frac{1}{2}$.

- Repeat these questions with different amounts. For example: Start at 12 and remove 7 halves. ($12 - \frac{7}{2} = ?$)

- Use the number lines provided for each activity (pages 67–70) to introduce subtracting thirds, fourths, fifths, and sixths.

Students are now ready for the **Fraction Number Line activities for Subtraction.**

LESSON 10: USING A NUMBER LINE TO DIVIDE (HAS HOW MANY) FRACTIONAL PARTS

- Copy the halves number line on the board (page 72) or display with a document camera. Each team should have their own copy of the halves number line.

- Say: *Move from 0 to 4 on your number lines. How many halves are there from 0 to 4?* OR: *4 has how many halves?* (8)

- Say: *Discuss with your partner and explain your thinking.*

- Have a student team demonstrate on the board how they determined the number of halves.

- Write on the board: $4 \div \frac{1}{2} = 8$.

- Repeat these questions with whole numbers and mixed numbers. For example: Seven has how many halves? (13) $8\frac{1}{2} \div \frac{1}{2} = ?$ (17) $15 \div \frac{1}{2} = ?$ (30)

- Pose these challenge questions: How many halves does 50 have? Or $50 \div \frac{1}{2} = ?$ (100) $100 \div = ? \ 200 \div \frac{1}{2} = ? \ 1000 \div \frac{1}{2} = ?$

- Say: *Discuss with your partner and explain your thinking.* Discuss class responses.

- Use the number lines provided for each activity (pages 73–76) to introduce dividing (has how many) thirds, fourths, fifths, and sixths.

Students are now ready for the **Fraction Number Line activities for Division (Has How Many).**

Fraction Number Line Activities – Score Chart
Adding/Multiplying, Subtracting

Die Toss	Fraction	Location on Number Line

Die Toss	Fraction	Location on Number Line

Die Toss	Fraction	Location on Number Line

	Score
Game 1	
Game 2	
Game 3	
Total Score	

Fraction Number Line – Adding/Multiplying Halves

How to Play

- Each team gets a score chart (page 60), number line, die, and pencil.

- Toss a die.

- Make a fraction: numerator = die toss, denominator = 2.

- Start at 0. Move ahead that many halves on the number line. (**Example:** Toss a 3. Fraction is $\frac{3}{2}$. Move ahead 3 halves.)

- On the score chart, record the die toss, the fraction created by the die toss, and the location on the number line.

- On the next die toss, move forward from that location on the number line.

- After 5 tosses, the score closest to $7\frac{1}{2}$ on the number line wins.

- Play 2 or more games. The first team to win 2 games is the winner.

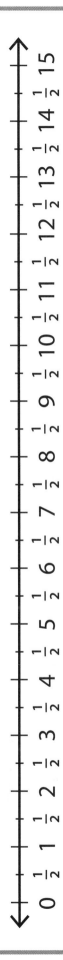

$0 \quad \frac{1}{2} \quad 1 \quad 1\frac{1}{2} \quad 2 \quad 2\frac{1}{2} \quad 3 \quad 3\frac{1}{2} \quad 4 \quad 4\frac{1}{2} \quad 5 \quad 5\frac{1}{2} \quad 6 \quad 6\frac{1}{2} \quad 7 \quad 7\frac{1}{2} \quad 8 \quad 8\frac{1}{2} \quad 9 \quad 9\frac{1}{2} \quad 10 \quad 10\frac{1}{2} \quad 11 \quad 11\frac{1}{2} \quad 12 \quad 12\frac{1}{2} \quad 13 \quad 13\frac{1}{2} \quad 14 \quad 14\frac{1}{2} \quad 15$

Fraction Number Line – Adding/Multiplying Thirds

How to Play

- Each team gets a score chart (page 60), number line, die, and pencil.

- Toss a die.

- Make a fraction: numerator = die toss, denominator = 3.

- Start at 0. Move ahead that many thirds on the number line. (**Example:** Toss a 3. Fraction is $\frac{5}{3}$. Move ahead 5 thirds.)

- On the score chart, record the die toss, the fraction created by the die toss, and the location on the number line.

- On the next die toss, move forward from that location on the number line.

- After 5 tosses, the score closest to 5 on the number line wins.

- Play 2 or more games. The first team to win 2 games is the winner.

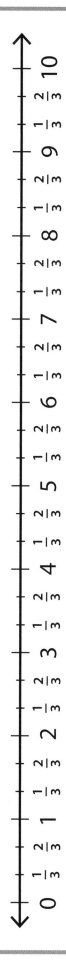

Fraction Number Line – Adding/Multiplying Fourths

How to Play

- Each team gets a score chart (page 60), number line, die, and pencil.

- Toss a die.

- Make a fraction: **numerator = die toss, denominator = 4.**

- Start at 0. Move ahead that many fourths on the number line. (**Example:** Toss a 5. Fraction is $\frac{5}{4}$. Move ahead 5 fourths.)

- On the score chart, record the die toss, the fraction created by the die toss, and the location on the number line.

- On the next die toss, move forward from that location on the number line.

- After 5 tosses, the score closest to $3\frac{3}{4}$ on the number line wins.

- Play 2 or more games. The first team to win 2 games is the winner.

Fraction Number Line – Adding/Multiplying Fifths

How to Play

- Each team gets a score chart (page 60), number line, die, and pencil.
- Toss a die.
- Make a fraction: **numerator = die toss, denominator = 5.**
- Start at 0. Move ahead that many fifths on the number line. (**Example:** Toss a 4. Fraction is $\frac{4}{5}$. **Move ahead 4 fifths.**)
- On the score chart, record the die toss, the fraction created by the die toss, and the location on the number line.
- On the next die toss, move forward from that location on the number line.
- After 5 tosses, the score closest to 3 on the number line wins.
- Play 2 or more games. The first team to win 2 games is the winner.

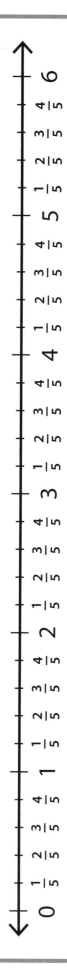

Fraction Number Line – Adding/Multiplying Sixths

How to Play

- Each team gets a score chart (page 60), number line, die, and pencil.
- Toss a die.
- Make a fraction: numerator = die toss, denominator = 6.
- Start at 0. Move **ahead** that many sixths on the number line. (**Example:** Toss a 5. Fraction is $\frac{5}{6}$. Move ahead 5 sixths.)
- On the score chart, record the die toss, the fraction created by the die toss, and the location on the number line.
- On the next die toss, move forward from that location on the number line.
- After 5 tosses, the score closest to $2\frac{3}{6}$ on the number line wins.
- Play 2 or more games. The first team to win 2 games is the winner.

Fraction Number Line – Subtracting Halves

How to Play

- Each team gets a score chart (page 60), number line, die, and pencil.

- Toss a die.

- Make a fraction: **numerator = die toss, denominator = 2.**

- Starting at 15, **move back** that many **halves** on the number line. Record the new location on the score chart. (**Example:** Toss a 4. Fraction is $\frac{4}{2}$. Move back 4 halves. Record the fraction $\frac{4}{2}$ and the location, 13.)

- On the next toss, move back from the current location to the next location on the number line. Record the toss and the new location on the score chart.

- After 5 tosses, the score closest to $7\frac{1}{2}$ on the number line wins.

- Play 2 or more games. The first team to win 2 games is the winner. OR:

- After 3 games, tally the 3 scores. The score closest to $22\frac{1}{2}$ wins.

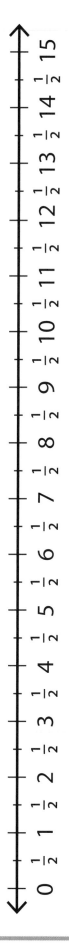

$0\frac{1}{2}$ 1 $1\frac{1}{2}$ 2 $2\frac{1}{2}$ 3 $3\frac{1}{2}$ 4 $4\frac{1}{2}$ 5 $5\frac{1}{2}$ 6 $6\frac{1}{2}$ 7 $7\frac{1}{2}$ 8 $8\frac{1}{2}$ 9 $9\frac{1}{2}$ 10 $10\frac{1}{2}$ 11 $11\frac{1}{2}$ 12 $12\frac{1}{2}$ 13 $13\frac{1}{2}$ 14 $14\frac{1}{2}$ 15

Fraction Number Line – Subtracting Thirds

How to Play

- Each team gets a score chart (page 60), number line, die, and pencil.
- Toss a die.
- Make a fraction: **numerator = die toss, denominator = 3.**
- Starting at 10, **move back** that many **thirds** on the number line.
- (**Example:** Toss a 5. Fraction is $\frac{5}{3}$. Move back 5 thirds. Record the fraction $\frac{5}{3}$ and the location, $8\frac{1}{3}$.)
- On the next toss, move back from the current location to the next location on the number line. Record the toss and the new location on the score chart.
- After 5 tosses, the score closest to **5** on the number line wins.
- Play 2 or more games. The first team to win 2 games is the winner. OR:
- After 3 games, tally the 3 scores. The score closest to **15** wins.

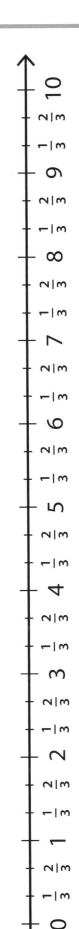

$0\frac{1}{3}$ 1 $1\frac{2}{3}$ $1\frac{1}{3}$ 2 $2\frac{2}{3}$ $2\frac{1}{3}$ 3 $3\frac{2}{3}$ $3\frac{1}{3}$ 4 $4\frac{2}{3}$ $4\frac{1}{3}$ 5 $5\frac{2}{3}$ $5\frac{1}{3}$ 6 $6\frac{2}{3}$ $6\frac{1}{3}$ 7 $7\frac{2}{3}$ $7\frac{1}{3}$ 8 $8\frac{2}{3}$ $8\frac{1}{3}$ 9 $9\frac{2}{3}$ $9\frac{1}{3}$ 10 $10\frac{2}{3}$

Fraction Number Line – Subtracting Fourths

How to Play

- Each team gets a score chart (page 60), number line, die, and pencil.

- Toss a die.

- Make a fraction: **numerator = die toss, denominator = 4.**

- Starting at $7\frac{2}{4}$, **move back** that many **fourths** on the number line. (**Example:** Toss a 2. Fraction is $\frac{2}{4}$. Move back 2 fourths. Record the fraction $\frac{2}{4}$ and the location, 7.)

- On the next toss, move back from the current location to the next location on the number line. Record the toss and the new location on the score chart.

- After 5 tosses, the score closest to $3\frac{3}{4}$ on the number line wins.

- Play 2 or more games. The first team to win 2 games is the winner. OR:

- After 3 games, tally the 3 scores. The score closest to $11\frac{1}{4}$ wins.

Fraction Number Line – Subtracting Fifths

How to Play

- Each team gets a score chart (page 60), number line, die, and pencil.
- Toss a die.
- Make a fraction: **numerator = die toss, denominator = 5.**
- Starting at 6, **move back** that many **fifths** on the number line. (**Example:** Toss a 6. Fraction is $\frac{6}{5}$. Move back 6 fifths. Record the fraction $\frac{6}{5}$ and the location, $4\frac{4}{5}$.)
- On the next toss, move back from the current location to the next location on the number line. Record the toss and the new location on the score chart.
- After 5 tosses, the score closest to **3** on the number line wins.
- Play 2 or more games. The first team to win 2 games is the winner. OR:
- After 3 games, tally the 3 scores. The score closest to **9** wins.

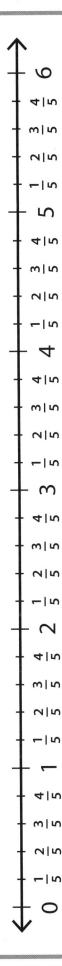

$0 \quad \frac{1}{5} \quad \frac{2}{5} \quad \frac{3}{5} \quad \frac{4}{5} \quad 1 \quad \frac{1}{5} \quad \frac{2}{5} \quad \frac{3}{5} \quad \frac{4}{5} \quad 2 \quad \frac{1}{5} \quad \frac{2}{5} \quad \frac{3}{5} \quad \frac{4}{5} \quad 3 \quad \frac{1}{5} \quad \frac{2}{5} \quad \frac{3}{5} \quad \frac{4}{5} \quad 4 \quad \frac{1}{5} \quad \frac{2}{5} \quad \frac{3}{5} \quad \frac{4}{5} \quad 5 \quad \frac{1}{5} \quad \frac{2}{5} \quad \frac{3}{5} \quad \frac{4}{5} \quad 6$

Fraction Number Line – Subtracting Sixths

How to Play

- Each team gets a score chart (page 60), number line, die, and pencil.

- Toss a die.

- Make a fraction: **numerator = die toss, denominator = 6.**

- Starting at 5, **move back** that many **sixths** on the number line. (**Example:** Toss a 5. Fraction is $\frac{5}{6}$. Move back 5 sixths. Record the fraction $\frac{5}{6}$ and the location, $4\frac{1}{6}$.)

- On the next toss, move back from the current location to the next location on the number line. Record the toss and the new location on the score chart.

- After 5 tosses, the score closest to $2\frac{3}{6}$ on the number line wins.

- Play 2 or more games. The first team to win 2 games is the winner. OR: After 3 games, tally the 3 scores. The score closest to $7\frac{3}{6}$ wins.

Die Toss	Fractional parts in toss	Score
	Total – Game 1	

Die Toss	Fractional parts in toss	Score
	Total – Game 2	

Die Toss	Fractional parts in toss	Score
	Total – Game 3	

	Score
Game 1	
Game 2	
Game 3	
Total Score	

Fraction Number Line – Has How Many Halves (Division)

How to Play

- Toss a die. Each team gets a score chart (page 71), number line, die, and pencil.

- Each dot = a whole number. Use the fraction number line to find out **how many halves** in the die toss number.

- **Example:** Toss 3. From 0 to 1, there are 2 of the halves. From 0 to 2, there are 4 of the halves. From 0 to 3, there are 6 of the halves. **The score is 6.**

- On the score chart, record the die toss, how many halves in the die toss number, and the score.

- After 5 tosses, the team score closest to **30** wins.

- Play 2 or more games. The first team to win 2 games is the winner. OR

- After 3 games, tally the 3 scores. The team score closest to **90** wins.

$$0 \quad \frac{1}{2} \quad 1 \quad 1\frac{1}{2} \quad 2 \quad 2\frac{1}{2} \quad 3 \quad 3\frac{1}{2} \quad 4 \quad 4\frac{1}{2} \quad 5 \quad 5\frac{1}{2} \quad 6 \quad 6\frac{1}{2} \quad 7 \quad 7\frac{1}{2} \quad 8 \quad 8\frac{1}{2} \quad 9 \quad 9\frac{1}{2} \quad 10 \quad 10\frac{1}{2} \quad 11 \quad 11\frac{1}{2} \quad 12 \quad 12\frac{1}{2} \quad 13 \quad 13\frac{1}{2} \quad 14 \quad 14\frac{1}{2} \quad 15$$

Fraction Number Line – Has How Many Thirds (Division)

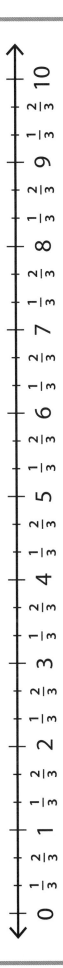

How to Play

- Toss a die. Each team gets a score chart (page 71), number line, die, and pencil.

- Each dot = a whole number. Use the fraction number line to find out **how many thirds** in the die toss number.

- **Example:** Toss 3. From 0 to 1, there are 3 of the thirds. From 0 to 2, there are 6 of the thirds. From 0 to 3, there are 9 of the thirds. **The score is 9.**

- On the score chart, record the die toss, how many thirds in the die toss number, and the score.

- After 5 tosses, the team score closest to **45** wins.

- Play 2 or more games. The first team to win 2 games is the winner. OR

- After 3 games, tally the 3 scores. The team score closest to **135** wins.

0 1 2 3 4 5 6 7 8 9 10

$\frac{1}{3}$ $\frac{2}{3}$ $1\frac{1}{3}$ $1\frac{2}{3}$ $2\frac{1}{3}$ $2\frac{2}{3}$ $3\frac{1}{3}$ $3\frac{2}{3}$ $4\frac{1}{3}$ $4\frac{2}{3}$ $5\frac{1}{3}$ $5\frac{2}{3}$ $6\frac{1}{3}$ $6\frac{2}{3}$ $7\frac{1}{3}$ $7\frac{2}{3}$ $8\frac{1}{3}$ $8\frac{2}{3}$ $9\frac{1}{3}$ $9\frac{2}{3}$

Fraction Number Line – Has How Many Fourths (Division)

How to Play

- Toss a die. Each team gets a score chart (page 71), number line, die, and pencil.

- Each dot = a whole number. Use the fraction number line to find out **how many fourths** in the die toss number.

- **Example:** Toss 3. From 0 to 1, there are 4 of the fourths. From 0 to 2, there are 8 of the fourths. From 0 to 3, there are 12 of the fourths. **The score is 12.**

- On the score chart, record the die toss, how many fourths in the die toss number, and the score.

- After 5 tosses, the team score closest to **60** wins.

- Play 2 or more games. The first team to win 2 games is the winner. OR

- After 3 games, tally the 3 scores. The team score closest to **180** wins.

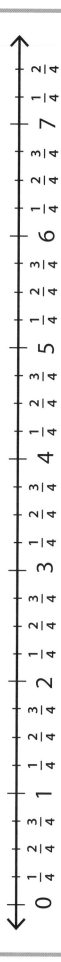

Fraction Number Line – Has How Many Fifths (Division)

How to Play

- Toss a die. Each team gets a score chart (page 71), number line, die, and pencil.

- Each dot = a whole number. Use the fraction number line to find out **how many fifths** in the die toss number.

- **Example:** Toss 3. From 0 to 1, there are 5 of the fifths. From 0 to 2, there are 10 of the fifths. From 0 to 3, there are 15 of the fifths. **The score is 15.**

- On the score chart, record the die toss, how many fifths in the die toss number, and the score.

- After 5 tosses, the team score closest to **75** wins.

- Play 2 or more games. The first team to win 2 games is the winner. OR

- After 3 games, tally the 3 scores. The team score closest to **225** wins.

Fraction Number Line – Has How Many Sixths (Division)

How to Play

- Toss a die. Each team gets a score chart (page 71), number line, die, and pencil.

- Each dot = a whole number. Use the fraction number line to find out **how many sixths** in the die toss number.

- **Example:** Toss 3. From 0 to 1, there are 6 of the sixths. From 0 to 2, there are 12 of the sixths. From 0 to 3, there are 18 of the sixths. **The score is 18.**

- On the score chart, record the die toss, how many sixths in the die toss number, and the score.

- After 5 tosses, the team score closest to **90** wins.

- Play 2 or more games. The first team to win 2 games is the winner. OR

- After 3 games, tally the 3 scores. The team score closest to **270** wins.

Fraction Games & Activities with Dice!

Equalities/Inequalities Activities

Contents

Notes to Teachers/Fraction Equalities and Inequalities

- Students understand relationships among fractions and the values of denominators.

- Students understand that a fraction with a smaller denominator is a larger quantity than a fraction with a larger denominator, assuming the numerator is constant.

Overview

The **Fraction Equalities/Inequalities activities** are "fill the chart" activities. Students toss 2 dice to make a proper fraction. Using the fraction chart provided on the activity page for reference, students determine whether the fraction is more than, less than, or equal to (<, >, +) a specific fraction on the chart. Students write the proper fraction in the appropriate box to make a true statement.

Each of the first five activities deal with a specific denominator—halves, thirds, fourths, fifths, and sixths. The last four activities involve more than one denominator.

Materials

- "Fraction Equalities/Inequalities" charts (pages 79–83)
- 2 colored pencils (different colors)
- 2 dice

Getting Started

Jump in and have fun!

- Teams share a chart.
- Teams toss a die.
- Higher number goes first.

How to Play

- **Toss 2 dice.** Using the two numbers tossed, **make a proper fraction or a fraction that equals 1.**

- Write the fraction in one of the spaces on the chart. Explain why the fraction makes the equation or inequality true.

- **Example:** Toss a 4 and a 6. Make the fraction $\frac{4}{6}$. Write the fraction in the box, $\frac{1}{2} < \frac{4}{6}$. Explain why the inequality is true. ("One-half is the same as $\frac{3}{6}$, and $\frac{3}{6}$ is less than $\frac{4}{6}$.")

- If it is not possible to place a fraction on the chart, the team loses a turn.

- The team that makes the most "true statements" wins.

1					
$\frac{1}{2}$			$\frac{1}{2}$		
$\frac{1}{3}$		$\frac{1}{3}$		$\frac{1}{3}$	
$\frac{1}{4}$		$\frac{1}{4}$	$\frac{1}{4}$		$\frac{1}{4}$
$\frac{1}{5}$	$\frac{1}{5}$	$\frac{1}{5}$	$\frac{1}{5}$		$\frac{1}{5}$
$\frac{1}{6}$	$\frac{1}{6}$	$\frac{1}{6}$	$\frac{1}{6}$	$\frac{1}{6}$	$\frac{1}{6}$

$\underline{\quad\quad} > \frac{1}{2}$	$\frac{1}{2} > \underline{\quad\quad}$	$\frac{1}{2} = \underline{\quad\quad}$
$\frac{1}{2} < \underline{\quad\quad}$	$\underline{\quad\quad} = \frac{2}{2}$	$\underline{\quad\quad} < \frac{1}{2}$
$\frac{1}{2} > \underline{\quad\quad}$	$\underline{\quad\quad} = \frac{1}{2}$	$\frac{1}{2} < \underline{\quad\quad}$
$\underline{\quad\quad} = \frac{1}{2}$	$\frac{1}{2} < \underline{\quad\quad}$	$\frac{1}{2} > \underline{\quad\quad}$
$\frac{1}{2} < \underline{\quad\quad}$	$\underline{\quad\quad} = \frac{2}{2}$	$\underline{\quad\quad} < \frac{1}{2}$

Fraction Equalities/Inequalities – Thirds

Lessons 3 & 4

- Teams share a chart.
- Teams toss a die.
- Higher number goes first.

How to Play

1					
$\frac{1}{2}$			$\frac{1}{2}$		
$\frac{1}{3}$		$\frac{1}{3}$		$\frac{1}{3}$	
$\frac{1}{4}$		$\frac{1}{4}$		$\frac{1}{4}$	$\frac{1}{4}$
$\frac{1}{5}$	$\frac{1}{5}$	$\frac{1}{5}$	$\frac{1}{5}$	$\frac{1}{5}$	
$\frac{1}{6}$	$\frac{1}{6}$	$\frac{1}{6}$	$\frac{1}{6}$	$\frac{1}{6}$	$\frac{1}{6}$

- **Toss 2 dice.** Using the two numbers tossed, **make a proper fraction or a fraction that equals 1.**

- Write the fraction in one of the spaces on the chart. Explain why the fraction makes the equation or inequality true.

- **Example:** Toss a 4 and a 6. Make the fraction $\frac{4}{6}$. Write the fraction in the box, $\frac{1}{3} < \frac{4}{6}$. Explain why the inequality is true. ("One-third is the same as $\frac{2}{6}$, and $\frac{2}{6}$ is less than $\frac{4}{6}$.")

- If it is not possible to place a fraction on the chart, the team loses a turn.

- The team that makes the most "true statements" wins.

$\underline{\quad} > \frac{1}{3}$	$\frac{1}{3} < \underline{\quad}$	$\frac{3}{3} = \underline{\quad}$
$\frac{1}{3} < \underline{\quad}$	$\underline{\quad} = \frac{2}{3}$	$\underline{\quad} > \frac{1}{3}$
$\frac{2}{3} > \underline{\quad}$	$\underline{\quad} = \frac{1}{3}$	$\frac{1}{3} < \underline{\quad}$
$\underline{\quad} = \frac{1}{3}$	$\frac{2}{3} < \underline{\quad}$	$\frac{1}{3} > \underline{\quad}$
$\frac{1}{3} < \underline{\quad}$	$\underline{\quad} = \frac{3}{3}$	$\underline{\quad} > \frac{1}{3}$

Fraction Games & Activities with Dice!

© Didax – www.didax.com

- Teams share a chart.
- Teams toss a die.
- Higher number goes first.

How to Play

1		
$\frac{1}{2}$		$\frac{1}{2}$
$\frac{1}{3}$	$\frac{1}{3}$	$\frac{1}{3}$
$\frac{1}{4}$	$\frac{1}{4}$	$\frac{1}{4}$ $\frac{1}{4}$
$\frac{1}{5}$	$\frac{1}{5}$ $\frac{1}{5}$ $\frac{1}{5}$	$\frac{1}{5}$
$\frac{1}{6}$	$\frac{1}{6}$ $\frac{1}{6}$ $\frac{1}{6}$ $\frac{1}{6}$	$\frac{1}{6}$

- **Toss 2 dice.** Using the two numbers tossed, **make a proper fraction or a fraction that equals 1.**

- Write the fraction in one of the spaces on the chart. Explain why the fraction makes the equation or inequality true.

- **Example:** Toss a 2 and a 6. Make the fraction $\frac{2}{6}$. Write the fraction in the box, $\frac{2}{6} > \frac{1}{4}$. Explain why the inequality is true. ("Two-sixths is the same as $\frac{1}{3}$, and $\frac{1}{3}$ is greater than $\frac{1}{4}$.")

- If it is not possible to place a fraction on the chart, the team loses a turn.

- The team that makes the most "true statements" wins.

$\underline{} > \frac{1}{4}$	$\frac{1}{4} < \underline{}$	$\frac{2}{4} = \underline{}$
$\frac{2}{4} < \underline{}$	$\underline{} = \frac{4}{4}$	$\underline{} > \frac{3}{4}$
$\frac{3}{4} > \underline{}$	$\underline{} = \frac{2}{4}$	$\frac{1}{4} < \underline{}$
$\underline{} = \frac{4}{4}$	$\frac{1}{4} < \underline{}$	$\frac{2}{4} > \underline{}$
$\frac{1}{4} > \underline{}$	$\underline{} = \frac{2}{4}$	$\underline{} < \frac{1}{4}$

- Teams share a chart.
- Teams toss a die.
- Higher number goes first.

How to Play

1					
$\frac{1}{2}$			$\frac{1}{2}$		
$\frac{1}{3}$		$\frac{1}{3}$		$\frac{1}{3}$	
$\frac{1}{4}$		$\frac{1}{4}$	$\frac{1}{4}$		$\frac{1}{4}$
$\frac{1}{5}$	$\frac{1}{5}$	$\frac{1}{5}$	$\frac{1}{5}$		$\frac{1}{5}$
$\frac{1}{6}$	$\frac{1}{6}$	$\frac{1}{6}$	$\frac{1}{6}$	$\frac{1}{6}$	$\frac{1}{6}$

- **Toss 2 dice.** Using the two numbers tossed, **make a proper fraction or a fraction that equals 1.**
- Write the fraction in one of the spaces on the chart. Explain why the fraction makes the equation or inequality true.
- **Example:** Toss a 2 and a 4. Make the fraction $\frac{2}{4}$. Write the fraction in the box, $\frac{2}{4} > \frac{2}{5}$. Explain why the inequality is true. ("Two-fourths is greater than $\frac{2}{5}$ because $\frac{1}{4}$ is greater than $\frac{1}{5}$.")
- If it is not possible to place a fraction on the chart, the team loses a turn.
- The team that makes the most "true statements" wins.

$\underline{\quad} > \frac{2}{5}$	$\frac{1}{5} < \underline{\quad}$	$\frac{3}{5} > \underline{\quad}$
$\frac{5}{5} = \underline{\quad}$	$\underline{\quad} > \frac{4}{5}$	$\underline{\quad} > \frac{2}{5}$
$\frac{2}{5} > \underline{\quad}$	$\underline{\quad} > \frac{3}{5}$	$\frac{4}{5} < \underline{\quad}$
$\underline{\quad} < \frac{2}{5}$	$\frac{5}{5} = \underline{\quad}$	$\frac{3}{5} > \underline{\quad}$
$\frac{1}{5} < \underline{\quad}$	$\underline{\quad} > \frac{3}{5}$	$\underline{\quad} < \frac{2}{5}$

Fraction Equalities/Inequalities – Sixths

- Teams share a chart.
- Teams toss a die.
- Higher number goes first.

How to Play

- **Toss 2 dice.** Using the two numbers tossed, **make a proper fraction or a fraction that equals 1.**
- Write the fraction in one of the spaces on the chart. Explain why the fraction makes the equation or inequality true.
- **Example:** Toss a **2** and a **3**. Make the fraction $\frac{2}{3}$. Write the fraction in the box, $\frac{2}{3} = \frac{4}{6}$. Explain why the inequality is true. ("Two-thirds is equivalent to $\frac{4}{6}$.")
- If it is not possible to place a fraction on the chart, the team loses a turn.
- The team that makes the most "true statements" wins.

1		
$\frac{1}{2}$		$\frac{1}{2}$
$\frac{1}{3}$	$\frac{1}{3}$	$\frac{1}{3}$
$\frac{1}{4}$ $\frac{1}{4}$	$\frac{1}{4}$	$\frac{1}{4}$
$\frac{1}{5}$ $\frac{1}{5}$	$\frac{1}{5}$	$\frac{1}{5}$ $\frac{1}{5}$
$\frac{1}{6}$ $\frac{1}{6}$	$\frac{1}{6}$ $\frac{1}{6}$	$\frac{1}{6}$ $\frac{1}{6}$

$\_\_\_ < \frac{4}{6}$	$\frac{3}{6} > \_\_\_$	$\frac{6}{6} = \_\_\_$
$\frac{2}{6} < \_\_\_$	$\_\_\_ = \frac{4}{6}$	$\_\_\_ < \frac{3}{6}$
$\frac{5}{6} > \_\_\_$	$\_\_\_ = \frac{6}{6}$	$\frac{4}{6} < \_\_\_$
$\_\_\_ = \frac{2}{6}$	$\frac{3}{6} < \_\_\_$	$\frac{5}{6} > \_\_\_$
$\frac{4}{6} > \_\_\_$	$\_\_\_ = \frac{3}{6}$	$\_\_\_ < \frac{4}{6}$

Fraction Equalities/Inequalities – Halves and Fourths

How to Play

- Teams share a chart.
- Teams toss a die.
- Higher number goes first.

1	
$\frac{1}{2}$	$\frac{1}{2}$
$\frac{1}{4}$ $\frac{1}{4}$	$\frac{1}{4}$ $\frac{1}{4}$

- Toss a die. Make a fraction. **Numerator = die toss, denominator = 4.**
- Write the fraction in a space on the chart. Explain why the fraction makes the inequality or equation true.
- **Example:** Toss a 3. Make the fraction $\frac{3}{4}$. Write the fraction in the box $\frac{3}{4} > \frac{1}{2}$. Explain why the inequality is true: "One-half is equivalent to $\frac{2}{4}$, and $\frac{3}{4}$ is greater than $\frac{2}{4}$."
- If it is not possible to place the fraction on the chart, the team loses a turn.
- The team that makes the most "true statements" wins.

___ $> \frac{1}{2}$	$\frac{1}{2} <$ ___	$\frac{1}{4} =$ ___
$\frac{1}{4} <$ ___	___ $= \frac{1}{2}$	___ $> \frac{2}{4}$
$\frac{2}{2} >$ ___	___ $= \frac{2}{4}$	$\frac{2}{4} <$ ___
___ $= \frac{2}{4}$	$\frac{1}{2} <$ ___	$\frac{4}{4} >$ ___
$\frac{3}{4} <$ ___	___ $= \frac{2}{2}$	___ $> \frac{1}{4}$

Fraction Equalities/Inequalities – Halves, Thirds, Sixths

- Teams share a chart.
- Teams toss a die.
- Higher number goes first.

How to Play

- Toss a die. Make a fraction. **Numerator = die toss, denominator = 6.**
- Write the fraction in a space on the chart. Explain why the fraction makes the inequality or equation true.
- **Example:** Toss a 3. Make the fraction $\frac{3}{6}$. Write the fraction in the box $\frac{3}{6} > \frac{1}{3}$. Explain why the inequality is true: "One-third is equivalent to $\frac{2}{6}$, and $\frac{3}{6}$ is greater than $\frac{2}{6}$."
- If it is not possible to place the fraction on the chart, the team loses a turn.
- The team that makes the most "true statements" wins.

1					
$\frac{1}{2}$			$\frac{1}{2}$		
$\frac{1}{3}$		$\frac{1}{3}$		$\frac{1}{3}$	
$\frac{1}{6}$	$\frac{1}{6}$	$\frac{1}{6}$	$\frac{1}{6}$	$\frac{1}{6}$	$\frac{1}{6}$

$\underline{\qquad} > \frac{1}{3}$	$\frac{1}{2} < \underline{\qquad}$	$\frac{1}{3} > \underline{\qquad}$
$\frac{1}{6} < \underline{\qquad}$	$\underline{\qquad} = \frac{1}{3}$	$\underline{\qquad} > \frac{1}{2}$
$\frac{1}{2} > \underline{\qquad}$	$\underline{\qquad} = \frac{1}{6}$	$\frac{1}{3} < \underline{\qquad}$
$\underline{\qquad} = \frac{2}{3}$	$\frac{2}{6} < \underline{\qquad}$	$\frac{5}{6} > \underline{\qquad}$
$\frac{2}{3} < \underline{\qquad}$	$\underline{\qquad} = \frac{2}{2}$	$\underline{\qquad} > \frac{2}{6}$

Fraction Equalities/Inequalities – Fourths, Eighths

How to Play

- Teams share a chart.
- Teams toss a die.
- Higher number goes first.

- Toss a die. Make a fraction. **Numerator = die toss, denominator = 8.**
- Write the fraction in a space on the chart. Explain why the fraction makes the inequality or equation true.
- **Example:** Toss a 3. Make the fraction $\frac{3}{8}$. Write the fraction in the box $\frac{3}{8} < \frac{1}{2}$. Explain why the inequality is true: "One-half is equivalent to $\frac{4}{8}$, and $\frac{3}{8}$ is less than $\frac{4}{8}$."
- If it is not possible to place the fraction on the chart, the team loses a turn.
- The team that makes the most "true statements" wins.

1							
$\frac{1}{2}$				$\frac{1}{2}$			
$\frac{1}{4}$		$\frac{1}{4}$		$\frac{1}{4}$		$\frac{1}{4}$	
$\frac{1}{8}$	$\frac{1}{8}$	$\frac{1}{8}$	$\frac{1}{8}$	$\frac{1}{8}$	$\frac{1}{8}$	$\frac{1}{8}$	$\frac{1}{8}$

$\underline{\quad} < \frac{1}{2}$	$\frac{2}{8} < \underline{\quad}$	$\frac{1}{4} = \underline{\quad}$
$\frac{1}{4} < \underline{\quad}$	$\underline{\quad} = \frac{1}{2}$	$\underline{\quad} > \frac{2}{4}$
$\frac{5}{8} > \underline{\quad}$	$\underline{\quad} = \frac{2}{4}$	$\frac{3}{4} < \underline{\quad}$
$\underline{\quad} = \frac{4}{8}$	$\frac{4}{8} < \underline{\quad}$	$\frac{4}{4} > \underline{\quad}$
$\frac{3}{4} < \underline{\quad}$	$\underline{\quad} = \frac{2}{2}$	$\underline{\quad} > \frac{1}{4}$

Fraction Equalities/Inequalities – Mixed Toss

Lessons 3 & 4

- Teams share a chart.
- Teams toss a die.
- Higher number goes first.

How to Play

- **Toss 2 dice.** Use the numbers tossed to **make a proper fraction or a fraction that equals 1.**
- Write the fraction in a space on the chart and explain why the fraction makes the inequality or equation true.
- **Example:** Toss a 5 and a 6. Make the fraction $\frac{5}{6}$. Write the fraction in the box $\frac{5}{6} > \frac{1}{2}$. Explain why the inequality is true: "One-half is the same as $\frac{3}{6}$, so $\frac{5}{6}$ is greater than $\frac{3}{6}$."
- If it is not possible to place the fraction on the chart, the team loses a turn.
- The team that makes the most "true statements" wins.

1		
$\frac{1}{2}$		$\frac{1}{2}$
$\frac{1}{3}$	$\frac{1}{3}$	$\frac{1}{3}$
$\frac{1}{4}$	$\frac{1}{4}$	$\frac{1}{4}$ $\frac{1}{4}$
$\frac{1}{5}$ $\frac{1}{5}$	$\frac{1}{5}$	$\frac{1}{5}$ $\frac{1}{5}$
$\frac{1}{6}$ $\frac{1}{6}$ $\frac{1}{6}$	$\frac{1}{6}$	$\frac{1}{6}$ $\frac{1}{6}$

_____ $> \frac{1}{2}$	$\frac{5}{6} >$ _____	$\frac{2}{3} =$ _____
$\frac{3}{4} >$ _____	_____ $= 1$	_____ $> \frac{3}{4}$
$\frac{2}{5} >$ _____	_____ $< \frac{1}{2}$	$\frac{1}{4} <$ _____
_____ $= \frac{1}{3}$	$\frac{1}{4} >$ _____	$\frac{3}{3} >$ _____
$\frac{4}{6} <$ _____	_____ $= \frac{1}{2}$	_____ $< \frac{2}{5}$

© Didax – www.didax.com

Fraction Games & Activities with Dice! 87

Improper Fractions to Mixed Numbers Activities

Notes to Teachers/Improper Fractions to Mixed Numbers

Objectives

- Students convert improper fractions to whole or mixed numbers.
- Students develop fluency in recognizing improper fractions as mixed numbers, laying the foundation for operating with fractions procedurally (+, −, ×, ÷).

Overview

Each **Improper Fractions to Mixed Numbers Graph activity** is paired with a **Four-Grid Tic-Tac-Toe activity.** In the Graph activity, students make an improper fraction by doubling the die toss to determine the numerator. Each graph focuses on a specific denominator: halves, thirds, fourths, fifths, or sixths.

Students record the fraction they created in the column above the equivalent fraction, whole number, or mixed number on the graph. The first team to write five fractions in a row, vertically or horizontally, after each team has had the same number of tosses, wins that round. The first team to win two out of three rounds wins the game.

The Four-Grid Tic-Tac-Toe activity gives students another opportunity to practice converting improper fractions to mixed numbers.

Materials

- "Improper Fractions to Mixed Number" charts (pages 91–100)
- Die
- Pencil

Getting Started

Jump in and have fun!

Double the Numerator – Halves Graph

How to Play

• Toss a die. Make a fraction. **Numerator = double the die toss; denominator = 2.**

• Write the fraction in the box above the equivalent fraction.

• **Example:** Toss 5. Double 5 to make the numerator 10. Make the fraction $\frac{10}{2}$. Convert the improper fraction $\frac{10}{2}$ to the whole number 2.

• Write $\frac{10}{2}$ above the 2 on the graph below.

• Use the halves chart to help you change improper fractions to mixed or whole numbers.

• The first team to write 5 fractions in a row, vertically or horizontally, **after each team has had the same number of tosses,** wins that round.

• Play 2 or more rounds. The first team to win 2 rounds is the winner.

$\frac{1}{2}$	$\frac{1}{2}$
$\frac{1}{2}$	$\frac{1}{2}$
$\frac{1}{2}$	$\frac{1}{2}$
$\frac{1}{2}$	$\frac{1}{2}$
$\frac{1}{2}$	$\frac{1}{2}$
$\frac{1}{2}$	$\frac{1}{2}$

4	**1**	**6**	**3**	**2**	**5**

- Each team chooses a colored token.
- Teams toss a die.
- Higher number goes first.

$\frac{1}{2}$	$\frac{1}{2}$
$\frac{1}{2}$	$\frac{1}{2}$
$\frac{1}{2}$	$\frac{1}{2}$
$\frac{1}{2}$	$\frac{1}{2}$
$\frac{1}{2}$	$\frac{1}{2}$
$\frac{1}{2}$	$\frac{1}{2}$

How to Play

- Toss a die. Make a fraction. **Numerator = double the die toss; denominator = 2. Example:** Toss 2. Double 2 to make the numerator 4. Make the fraction $\frac{8}{4}$. Convert the improper fraction $\frac{8}{4}$ to the equivalent whole number, 2.
- Place a token on that whole number or mixed number on any of the 4 Tic-Tac-Toe grids.
- If the equivalent whole number or mixed number is not available, lose that turn.
- The team with the most "threes in a row" wins.

3	1	2		5	4	6
2	6	5		4	2	1
6	3	4		1	3	5
5	6	2		1	4	3
4	1	5		3	6	2
3	2	6		4	1	5

Double the Numerator – Thirds Graph

How to Play

- Each team gets a graph.
- Teams toss a die.
- Higher number goes first.

- Toss a die. Make a fraction. **Numerator = double the die toss; denominator = 3.**
- Write the fraction in the box above the equivalent fraction.
- **Example:** Toss 2. Double 2 to make the numerator 4. Make the fraction $\frac{4}{3}$. Convert the improper fraction $\frac{4}{3}$ to the mixed number $1\frac{1}{3}$.
- Write $\frac{4}{3}$ above the $1\frac{1}{3}$ on the graph below.
- Use the thirds chart to help you change improper fractions to mixed or whole numbers.
- The first team to write 5 fractions in a row, vertically or horizontally, **after each team has had the same number of tosses,** wins that round.
- Play 2 or more rounds. The first team to win 2 rounds is the winner.

$\frac{1}{3}$	$\frac{1}{3}$
$\frac{1}{3}$	$\frac{1}{3}$
$\frac{1}{3}$	$\frac{1}{3}$
$\frac{1}{3}$	$\frac{1}{3}$

$2\frac{2}{3}$	4	$3\frac{1}{3}$	$\frac{2}{3}$	2	$1\frac{1}{3}$

- Each team chooses a colored token.
- Teams toss a die.
- Higher number goes first.

How to Play

- Toss a die. Make a fraction. **Numerator = double the die toss; denominator = 3. Example:** Toss 2. Double 2 to make the numerator 4. Make the fraction $\frac{4}{3}$. Convert the improper fraction $\frac{4}{3}$ to the equivalent mixed number, $1\frac{1}{3}$.
- Place a token on that number on any of the 4 Tic-Tac-Toe grids.
- If the equivalent whole number or mixed number is not available, lose that turn.
- The team with the most "threes in a row" wins.

$\frac{1}{3}$	$\frac{1}{3}$	$\frac{1}{3}$
$\frac{1}{3}$	$\frac{1}{3}$	$\frac{1}{3}$
$\frac{1}{3}$	$\frac{1}{3}$	$\frac{1}{3}$
$\frac{1}{3}$	$\frac{1}{3}$	$\frac{1}{3}$

$3\frac{1}{3}$	$1\frac{1}{3}$	2	$2\frac{2}{3}$	4	$\frac{2}{3}$
2	$2\frac{2}{3}$	$\frac{2}{3}$	4	2	$1\frac{1}{3}$
$\frac{2}{3}$	$3\frac{1}{3}$	4	$1\frac{1}{3}$	$3\frac{1}{3}$	$2\frac{2}{3}$
$2\frac{2}{3}$	$\frac{2}{3}$	2	$1\frac{1}{3}$	4	$3\frac{1}{3}$
4	$1\frac{1}{3}$	$2\frac{2}{3}$	$3\frac{1}{3}$	$\frac{2}{3}$	2
$3\frac{1}{3}$	2	$\frac{2}{3}$	4	$1\frac{1}{3}$	$2\frac{2}{3}$

Double the Numerator – Fourths Graph

- Each team gets a graph.
- Teams toss a die.
- Higher number goes first.

How to Play

- Toss a die. Make a fraction. **Numerator = double the die toss; denominator = 4.**
- Write the fraction in the box above the equivalent fraction.
- **Example:** Toss 3. Double 3 to make the numerator 6. Make the fraction $\frac{6}{4}$. Convert the improper fraction $\frac{6}{4}$ to the mixed number $1\frac{2}{4}$ or $1\frac{1}{2}$.
- Write $\frac{6}{4}$ above the $1\frac{1}{2}$ on the graph below.
- Use the halves and fourths chart to help you change improper fractions to mixed or whole numbers.
- The first team to write 5 fractions in a row, vertically or horizontally, **after each team has had the same number of tosses,** wins that round.
- Play 2 or more rounds. The first team to win 2 rounds is the winner.

$\frac{1}{2}$		$\frac{1}{2}$	
$\frac{1}{4}$	$\frac{1}{4}$	$\frac{1}{4}$	$\frac{1}{4}$
$\frac{1}{4}$	$\frac{1}{4}$	$\frac{1}{4}$	$\frac{1}{4}$
$\frac{1}{4}$	$\frac{1}{4}$	$\frac{1}{4}$	$\frac{1}{4}$

$\frac{1}{2}$	**1**	**3**	$2\frac{1}{2}$	**2**	$1\frac{1}{2}$

- Each team chooses a colored token.
- Teams toss a die.
- Higher number goes first.

How to Play

$\frac{1}{2}$		$\frac{1}{2}$	
$\frac{1}{4}$	$\frac{1}{4}$	$\frac{1}{4}$	$\frac{1}{4}$
$\frac{1}{4}$	$\frac{1}{4}$	$\frac{1}{4}$	$\frac{1}{4}$
$\frac{1}{4}$	$\frac{1}{4}$	$\frac{1}{4}$	$\frac{1}{4}$

- Toss a die. Make a fraction. **Numerator = double the die toss; denominator = 4. Example:** Toss 3. Double 3 to make the numerator 6. Make the fraction $\frac{6}{4}$. Convert the improper fraction $\frac{6}{4}$ to the equivalent mixed number, $1\frac{2}{4}$ or $1\frac{1}{2}$.
- Place a token on that number on any of the 4 Tic-Tac-Toe grids.
- If the equivalent whole number or mixed number is not available, lose that turn.
- The team with the most "threes in a row" wins.

3	1	2		$2\frac{1}{2}$	$1\frac{2}{4}$	$\frac{1}{2}$
2	$\frac{1}{2}$	$2\frac{2}{4}$		$1\frac{1}{2}$	2	1
$\frac{1}{2}$	3	$1\frac{1}{2}$		1	3	$2\frac{2}{4}$
$2\frac{2}{4}$	$\frac{1}{2}$	2		1	$1\frac{2}{4}$	3
$1\frac{2}{4}$	1	$2\frac{1}{2}$		3	$\frac{1}{2}$	2
3	2	$\frac{1}{2}$		$1\frac{1}{2}$	1	$2\frac{2}{4}$

Double the Numerator – Fifths Graph

- Each team gets a graph.
- Teams toss a die.
- Higher number goes first.

How to Play

- Toss a die. Make a fraction. **Numerator = double the die toss; denominator = 5.**
- Write the fraction in the box above the equivalent fraction.
- **Example:** Toss 3. Double 3 to make the numerator 6. Make the fraction $\frac{6}{5}$. Convert the improper fraction $\frac{6}{5}$ to the mixed number $1\frac{1}{5}$.
- Write $\frac{6}{5}$ above the $1\frac{1}{5}$ on the graph below.
- Use the fifths chart to help you change improper fractions to mixed or whole numbers.
- The first team to write 5 fractions in a row, vertically or horizontally, **after each team has had the same number of tosses,** wins that round.
- Play 2 or more rounds. The first team to win 2 rounds is the winner.

$\frac{1}{5}$	$\frac{1}{5}$	$\frac{1}{5}$	$\frac{1}{5}$	$\frac{1}{5}$
$\frac{1}{5}$	$\frac{1}{5}$	$\frac{1}{5}$	$\frac{1}{5}$	$\frac{1}{5}$
$\frac{1}{5}$	$\frac{1}{5}$	$\frac{1}{5}$	$\frac{1}{5}$	$\frac{1}{5}$

$2\frac{2}{5}$	$\frac{4}{5}$	$1\frac{3}{5}$	$\frac{2}{5}$	2	$1\frac{1}{5}$

- Each team chooses a colored token.
- Teams toss a die.
- Higher number goes first.

How to Play

- Toss a die. Make a fraction. **Numerator = double the die toss; denominator = 5. Example:** Toss 3. Double 3 to make the numerator 6. Make the fraction $\frac{6}{5}$. Convert the improper fraction $\frac{6}{5}$ to the equivalent mixed number, $1\frac{1}{5}$.
- Place a token on that number on any of the 4 Tic-Tac-Toe grids.
- If the equivalent whole number or mixed number is not available, lose that turn.
- The team with the most "threes in a row" wins.

$\frac{1}{5}$	$\frac{1}{5}$	$\frac{1}{5}$	$\frac{1}{5}$	$\frac{1}{5}$
$\frac{1}{5}$	$\frac{1}{5}$	$\frac{1}{5}$	$\frac{1}{5}$	$\frac{1}{5}$
$\frac{1}{5}$	$\frac{1}{5}$	$\frac{1}{5}$	$\frac{1}{5}$	$\frac{1}{5}$

$\frac{4}{5}$	$1\frac{1}{5}$	2		$2\frac{2}{5}$	$1\frac{3}{5}$	$\frac{2}{5}$
2	$2\frac{2}{5}$	$\frac{2}{5}$		$1\frac{3}{5}$	2	$1\frac{1}{5}$
$\frac{2}{5}$	$\frac{4}{5}$	$1\frac{3}{5}$		$1\frac{1}{5}$	$\frac{4}{5}$	$2\frac{2}{5}$
$2\frac{2}{5}$	$\frac{2}{5}$	2		$1\frac{1}{5}$	$1\frac{3}{5}$	$\frac{4}{5}$
$1\frac{3}{5}$	$1\frac{1}{5}$	$2\frac{2}{5}$		$\frac{4}{5}$	$\frac{2}{5}$	2
$\frac{4}{5}$	2	$\frac{2}{5}$		$1\frac{3}{5}$	$1\frac{1}{5}$	$2\frac{2}{5}$

Double the Numerator – Sixths Graph

- Each team gets a graph.
- Teams toss a die.
- Higher number goes first.

How to Play

- Toss a die. Make a fraction. **Numerator = double the die toss; denominator = 6.**
- Write the fraction in the box above the equivalent fraction.
- **Example:** Toss 4. Double 4 to make the numerator 8. Make the fraction $\frac{8}{6}$. Convert the improper fraction $\frac{8}{6}$ to the mixed number $1\frac{2}{6}$ or $1\frac{1}{3}$.
- Write $\frac{8}{6}$ above the $1\frac{1}{3}$ on the graph below.
- Use the thirds and sixths chart to help you change improper fractions to mixed or whole numbers.
- The first team to write 5 fractions in a row, vertically or horizontally, **after each team has had the same number of tosses,** wins that round.
- Play 2 or more rounds. The first team to win 2 rounds is the winner.

$\frac{1}{3}$		$\frac{1}{3}$		$\frac{1}{3}$	
$\frac{1}{6}$	$\frac{1}{6}$	$\frac{1}{6}$	$\frac{1}{6}$	$\frac{1}{6}$	$\frac{1}{6}$
$\frac{1}{6}$	$\frac{1}{6}$	$\frac{1}{6}$	$\frac{1}{6}$	$\frac{1}{6}$	$\frac{1}{6}$

$\frac{2}{3}$	2	$1\frac{1}{3}$	$\frac{1}{3}$	1	$1\frac{2}{3}$

- Each team chooses a colored token.
- Teams toss a die.
- Higher number goes first.

How to Play

- Toss a die. Make a fraction. **Numerator = double the die toss; denominator = 6. Example:** Toss 4. Double 4 to make the numerator 8. Make the fraction $\frac{8}{6}$. Convert the improper fraction $\frac{8}{6}$ to the equivalent mixed number, $1\frac{2}{6}$ or $1\frac{1}{3}$.
- Place a token on that number on any of the 4 Tic-Tac-Toe grids.
- If the equivalent whole number or mixed number is not available, lose that turn.
- The team with the most "threes in a row" wins.

$\frac{1}{3}$	$\frac{1}{3}$	$\frac{1}{3}$

$\frac{1}{6}$	$\frac{1}{6}$	$\frac{1}{6}$	$\frac{1}{6}$	$\frac{1}{6}$	$\frac{1}{6}$
$\frac{1}{6}$	$\frac{1}{6}$	$\frac{1}{6}$	$\frac{1}{6}$	$\frac{1}{6}$	$\frac{1}{6}$

$\frac{2}{6}$	$1\frac{2}{6}$	2	$1\frac{4}{6}$	1	$\frac{2}{3}$
2	$1\frac{1}{3}$	$\frac{2}{3}$	1	2	$1\frac{2}{6}$
$\frac{4}{6}$	$\frac{1}{3}$	1	$1\frac{1}{3}$	$\frac{1}{3}$	$1\frac{2}{3}$
$1\frac{2}{3}$	$\frac{4}{6}$	2	$1\frac{1}{3}$	1	$\frac{1}{3}$
1	$1\frac{1}{3}$	$1\frac{4}{6}$	$\frac{2}{6}$	$\frac{2}{3}$	2
$\frac{1}{3}$	2	$\frac{2}{3}$	1	$1\frac{2}{6}$	$1\frac{2}{3}$

Equivalent Fractions
Graph Activities

Contents

Notes to Teachers/Equivalent Fractions Graph Activities

Objectives

- Students understand that any fraction $\frac{n}{n}$ equals 1, and that multiplying any number by $\frac{n}{n}$ (1) equals the number, or $\frac{a \times n}{b \times n} = \frac{an}{bn}$ $\quad \frac{1 \times 2}{2 \times 2} = \frac{2}{4}$.

Overview

In these **Equivalent Fractions Graph activities,** students make equivalent fractions for a specific denominator and record an equivalent fraction on the graph. As in the Section 5 activities, the first team to write five fractions in a row, either horizontally or vertically, after each team has had an equal number of turns, wins the round. The team that wins two out of three rounds wins the game.

Materials

- Graph activities (pages 103–108)
- Die
- Pencil

Getting Started

Refer to Lesson 4 (pages 13–14) for a review of fraction equivalence, if necessary.

Equivalent Fractions – Halves Graph

How to Play

- Toss a die. Find that number on the graph. Write a fraction that is equivalent to $\frac{1}{2}$ in the column above the number.

- **Example:** Toss 5. Write an equivalent fraction for $\frac{1}{2}$ in the column above 5 on the graph.

- To create a fraction equivalent to $\frac{1}{2}$, multiply $\frac{1}{2}$ by any fractions that $= 1$. **Example:** $\frac{1 \times 7}{2 \times 7} = \frac{7}{14}$.

- **Caution!** No team can repeat a fraction on their graph. Teams check each other's answers. If a mistake is made, that team loses a turn.

- The first team to write 5 fractions in a row, vertically or horizontally, **after each team has had the same number of tosses,** wins that round.

- The first team to win 2 out of 3 rounds wins the game.

4	**1**	**6**	**3**	**2**	**5**

Equivalent Fractions – Thirds Graph

- Each team gets a graph.
- Teams toss a die.
- Higher number goes first.

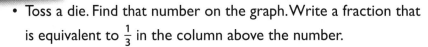
How to Play

- Toss a die. Find that number on the graph. Write a fraction that is equivalent to $\frac{1}{3}$ in the column above the number.

- **Example:** Toss 5. Write an equivalent fraction for $\frac{1}{3}$ in the column above 5 on the graph.

- To create a fraction equivalent to $\frac{1}{3}$, multiply $\frac{1}{3}$ by any fractions that $= 1$. **Example:** $\frac{1 \times 7}{3 \times 7} = \frac{7}{21}$.

- **Caution!** No team can repeat a fraction on their graph. Teams check each other's answers. If a mistake is made, that team loses a turn.

- The first team to write 5 fractions in a row, vertically or horizontally, **after each team has had the same number of tosses,** wins that round.

- The first team to win 2 out of 3 rounds wins the game.

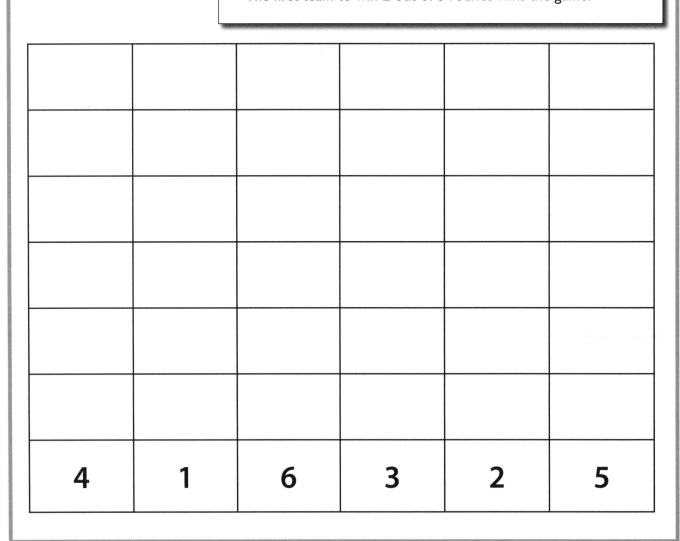

4	1	6	3	2	5

Equivalent Fractions – Fourths Graph

- Each team gets a graph.
- Teams toss a die.
- Higher number goes first.

How to Play

- Toss a die. Find that number on the graph. Write a fraction that is equivalent to $\frac{1}{4}$ in the column above the number.

- **Example:** Toss 5. Write an equivalent fraction for $\frac{1}{4}$ in the column above 5 on the graph.

- To create a fraction equivalent to $\frac{1}{4}$, multiply $\frac{1}{4}$ by any fraction that = 1. **Example:** $\frac{1 \times 7}{4 \times 7} = \frac{7}{28}$.

- **Caution!** No team can repeat a fraction on their graph. Teams check each other's answers. If a mistake is made, that team loses a turn.

- The first team to write 5 fractions in a row, vertically or horizontally, **after each team has had the same number of tosses,** wins that round.

- The first team to win 2 out of 3 rounds wins the game.

4	**1**	**6**	**3**	**2**	**5**

- Each team gets a graph.
- Teams toss a die.
- Higher number goes first.

Equivalent Fractions – Fifths Graph

How to Play

- Toss a die. Find that number on the graph. Write a fraction that is equivalent to $\frac{1}{5}$ in the column above the number.

- **Example:** Toss 5. Write an equivalent fraction for $\frac{1}{5}$ in the column above 5 on the graph.

- To create a fraction equivalent to $\frac{1}{5}$, multiply $\frac{1}{5}$ by any fractions that = 1. **Example:** $\frac{1 \times 7}{5 \times 7} = \frac{7}{35}$.

- **Caution!** No team can repeat a fraction on their graph. Teams check each other's answers. If a mistake is made, that team loses a turn.

- The first team to write 5 fractions in a row, vertically or horizontally, **after each team has had the same number of tosses,** wins that round.

- The first team to win 2 out of 3 rounds wins the game.

4	**1**	**6**	**3**	**2**	**5**

- Each team gets a graph.
- Teams toss a die.
- Higher number goes first.

How to Play

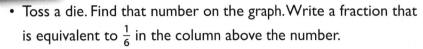

- Toss a die. Find that number on the graph. Write a fraction that is equivalent to $\frac{1}{6}$ in the column above the number.

- **Example:** Toss 5. Write an equivalent fraction for $\frac{1}{6}$ in the column above 5 on the graph.

- To create a fraction equivalent to $\frac{1}{6}$, multiply $\frac{1}{6}$ by any fractions that = 1. **Example:** $\frac{1 \times 7}{6 \times 7} = \frac{7}{42}$.

- **Caution!** No team can repeat a fraction on their graph. Teams check each other's answers. If a mistake is made, that team loses a turn.

- The first team to write 5 fractions in a row, vertically or horizontally, **after each team has had the same number of tosses,** wins that round.

- The first team to win 2 out of 3 rounds wins the game.

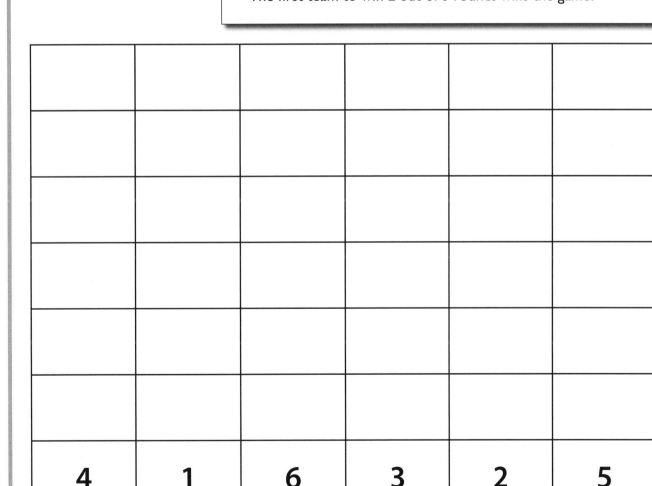

| 4 | 1 | 6 | 3 | 2 | 5 |

- Each team gets a graph.
- Teams toss a die.
- Higher number goes first.

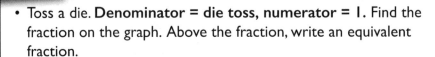

How to Play

- Toss a die. **Denominator = die toss, numerator = 1.** Find the fraction on the graph. Above the fraction, write an equivalent fraction.

- **Example:** Toss 5, make the fraction $\frac{1}{5}$. In the $\frac{1}{5}$ column, write an equivalent fraction, such as $\frac{2}{10}$.

- **Caution!** No team can repeat a fraction on their graph. Teams check each other's answers. If a mistake is made, that team loses a turn.

- The first team to write 5 fractions in a row, vertically or horizontally, **after each team has had the same number of tosses,** wins that round.

- The first team to win 2 out of 3 rounds wins the game.

$\frac{1}{4}$	**1**	$\frac{1}{6}$	$\frac{1}{3}$	$\frac{1}{2}$	$\frac{1}{5}$

Inequality/Equality Challenge Activities

Contents

Objectives

• Students synthesize their knowledge of fraction concepts at a more challenging level.

Overview

The **Inequality/Equality Challenge activities** are fill-in-the-chart activities. The first four activities are called **Alternative Expressions** because the chart contains alternative names for proper fractions, improper fractions, and mixed numbers.

Each activity has a specific denominator—halves, thirds, fourths, fifths, or sixths. Students toss a die, double the number tossed, and that becomes the numerator. Students write that fraction in an appropriate box on the chart to make a true statement. The next five activities are a bit more challenging because the signs now involve ≤ and ≥, along with some fun using ≠.

Materials

• "Inequality/Equality Challenge Activities" charts (pages 111–119)

• Die

• Colored pencils (different colored for each team)

Getting Started

There are many ways to begin this section. A powerful way would be for you to demonstrate the activities and challenge different teams to compete against "the teacher." The students may win more often than not, and this is a good sign.

Trust your students to figure it out. We trust you to continue to ask open-ended questions that invite your students to come to solutions with their student partners and study groups. Remember, at all times, that learning is open-ended and meant to foster inquisitive minds.

Alternative Expressions – Thirds

- Teams share a chart.
- Each team tosses a die.
- Higher number goes first.

How to Play

- Toss a die. Make a fraction. **Numerator = double the die toss; denominator = 3.**
- Write the fraction in one of the spaces on the chart. Explain why the fraction makes the equation or inequality true.
- **Example:** Toss a 2. Double it. Make the fraction $\frac{4}{3}$. Write the fraction in the box, $\frac{4}{3} > \frac{1}{3}$. Explain why the statement is true.
- If it is not possible to place a fraction on the chart, the team loses a turn.
- The team that makes the most "true statements" wins.

$\frac{1}{3}$	$\frac{1}{3}$	$\frac{1}{3}$
$\frac{1}{3}$	$\frac{1}{3}$	$\frac{1}{3}$
$\frac{1}{3}$	$\frac{1}{3}$	$\frac{1}{3}$
$\frac{1}{3}$	$\frac{1}{3}$	$\frac{1}{3}$

_____ $> \frac{1}{3}$	$\frac{4}{3} <$ _____	$2 =$ _____
$\frac{7}{3} <$ _____	_____ $= 2\frac{2}{3}$	_____ $< 1\frac{1}{3}$
$\frac{2}{3} <$ _____	_____ $= 1\frac{1}{3}$	$1\frac{5}{3} <$ _____
_____ $= 3\frac{3}{3}$	$\frac{2}{3} =$ _____	$3\frac{2}{3} >$ _____
$\frac{6}{3} <$ _____	_____ $= 2\frac{4}{3}$	_____ < 2

- Teams share a chart.
- Each team tosses a die.
- Higher number goes first.

How to Play

- Toss a die. Make a fraction. **Numerator = double the die toss; denominator = 4.**

- Write the fraction in one of the spaces on the chart. Explain why the fraction makes the equation or inequality true.

- **Example:** Toss a 3. Double it. Make the fraction $\frac{6}{4}$. Write the fraction in the box, $1\frac{1}{2} = \frac{6}{4}$. Explain why the statement is true.

- If it is not possible to place a fraction on the chart, the team loses a turn.

- The team that makes the most "true statements" wins.

1			
$\frac{1}{2}$		$\frac{1}{2}$	
$\frac{1}{4}$	$\frac{1}{4}$	$\frac{1}{4}$	$\frac{1}{4}$
$\frac{1}{4}$	$\frac{1}{4}$	$\frac{1}{4}$	$\frac{1}{4}$
$\frac{1}{4}$	$\frac{1}{4}$	$\frac{1}{4}$	$\frac{1}{4}$

$\underline{\qquad} = \frac{1}{2}$	$\frac{1}{1} < \underline{\qquad}$	$1\frac{4}{4} = \underline{\qquad}$
$2\frac{3}{4} < \underline{\qquad}$	$\underline{\qquad} = 1\frac{6}{4}$	$\underline{\qquad} > 1\frac{2}{4}$
$\frac{2}{4} < \underline{\qquad}$	$\underline{\qquad} = 2\frac{4}{4}$	$1\frac{1}{2} < \underline{\qquad}$
$\underline{\qquad} < 1\frac{6}{4}$	$1\frac{1}{2} > \underline{\qquad}$	$1\frac{8}{4} > \underline{\qquad}$
$\frac{8}{4} < \underline{\qquad}$	$\underline{\qquad} = \frac{4}{4}$	$\underline{\qquad} > 1\frac{6}{4}$

Alternative Expressions – Fifths

- Teams share a chart.
- Each team tosses a die.
- Higher number goes first.

How to Play

1				
$\frac{1}{5}$	$\frac{1}{5}$	$\frac{1}{5}$	$\frac{1}{5}$	$\frac{1}{5}$
$\frac{1}{5}$	$\frac{1}{5}$	$\frac{1}{5}$	$\frac{1}{5}$	$\frac{1}{5}$
$\frac{1}{5}$	$\frac{1}{5}$	$\frac{1}{5}$	$\frac{1}{5}$	$\frac{1}{5}$

- Toss a die. Make a fraction. **Numerator = double the die toss; denominator = 5.**
- Write the fraction in one of the spaces on the chart. Explain why the fraction makes the equation or inequality true.
- **Example:** Toss a 3. Double it. Make the fraction $\frac{6}{5}$. Write the fraction in the box, $\frac{6}{5} > \frac{2}{5}$. Explain why the statement is true.
- If it is not possible to place a fraction on the chart, the team loses a turn.
- The team that makes the most "true statements" wins.

$\underline{\quad} > \frac{2}{5}$	$\frac{1}{1} < \underline{\quad}$	$1\frac{5}{5} = \underline{\quad}$
$1\frac{3}{5} < \underline{\quad}$	$\underline{\quad} < \frac{10}{5}$	$\underline{\quad} = 1\frac{7}{5}$
$\frac{4}{5} > \underline{\quad}$	$\underline{\quad} = 1\frac{7}{5}$	$2 < \underline{\quad}$
$\underline{\quad} < \frac{6}{5}$	$2\frac{2}{5} > \underline{\quad}$	$\frac{5}{5} > \underline{\quad}$
$1\frac{3}{5} > \underline{\quad}$	$\underline{\quad} = 1\frac{3}{5}$	$\underline{\quad} < 1\frac{7}{5}$

Alternative Expressions – Sixths

How to Play

- Teams share a chart.
- Each team tosses a die.
- Higher number goes first.

- Toss a die. Make a fraction. **Numerator = double the die toss; denominator = 6.**
- Write the fraction in one of the spaces on the chart. Explain why the fraction makes the equation or inequality true.
- **Example:** Toss a 4. Double it. Make the fraction $\frac{8}{6}$. Write the fraction in the box, $\frac{8}{6} > \frac{2}{6}$. Explain why the statement is true.
- If it is not possible to place a fraction on the chart, the team loses a turn.
- The team that makes the most "true statements" wins.

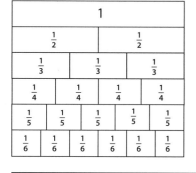

_____ $> \dfrac{1}{3}$	$\dfrac{2}{3} <$ _____	$1\dfrac{6}{6} =$ _____
$1\dfrac{2}{3} >$ _____	_____ $> \dfrac{6}{6}$	_____ $= 1\dfrac{4}{6}$
$1\dfrac{4}{6} >$ _____	_____ $= 1\dfrac{1}{3}$	$1\dfrac{1}{2} <$ _____
_____ $< \dfrac{6}{6}$	$\dfrac{1}{3} =$ _____	$\dfrac{8}{6} >$ _____
$1\dfrac{2}{6} <$ _____	_____ $= \dfrac{5}{5}$	_____ $< 1\dfrac{2}{3}$

Inequality/Equality – Halves Challenge

- Teams share a chart.
- Each team tosses a die.
- Higher number goes first.

How to Play

- Toss 2 dice. Make a fraction with the numbers tossed. Your fraction must be a **proper fraction or a fraction that equals 1.**
- Write the fraction in one of the spaces on the chart. Explain why the fraction makes the equation or inequality true.
- **Example:** Toss a 2 and a 4. Make the fraction $\frac{2}{4}$. Write the fraction in the box, $\frac{2}{4} \geq \frac{1}{2}$. Explain why the statement is true.
- If it is not possible to place a fraction on the chart, the team loses a turn.
- The team that makes the most "true statements" wins.

	1	
$\frac{1}{2}$		$\frac{1}{2}$

$\frac{1}{3}$	$\frac{1}{3}$	$\frac{1}{3}$

$\frac{1}{4}$	$\frac{1}{4}$	$\frac{1}{4}$	$\frac{1}{4}$

$\frac{1}{5}$	$\frac{1}{5}$	$\frac{1}{5}$	$\frac{1}{5}$	$\frac{1}{5}$

$\frac{1}{6}$	$\frac{1}{6}$	$\frac{1}{6}$	$\frac{1}{6}$	$\frac{1}{6}$	$\frac{1}{6}$

_____ $\geq \frac{1}{2}$	$\frac{1}{2} >$ _____	$\frac{1}{2} \neq$ _____
$\frac{1}{2} \leq$ _____	_____ $= \frac{2}{2}$	_____ $\geq \frac{1}{2}$
$\frac{1}{2} \geq$ _____	_____ $\neq \frac{1}{2}$	$\frac{1}{2} \leq$ _____
_____ $= \frac{1}{2}$	$\frac{1}{2} \geq$ _____	$\frac{1}{2} >$ _____
$\frac{1}{2} \leq$ _____	_____ $\neq \frac{2}{2}$	_____ $< \frac{1}{2}$

Inequality/Equality – Thirds Challenge

- Teams share a chart.
- Each team tosses a die.
- Higher number goes first.

How to Play

- Toss 2 dice. Make a fraction with the numbers tossed. Your fraction must be a **proper fraction or a fraction that equals 1**.

- Write the fraction in one of the spaces on the chart. Explain why the fraction makes the equation or inequality true.

- **Example:** Toss a 2 and a 4. Make the fraction $\frac{2}{4}$. Write the fraction in the box, $\frac{2}{4} \geq \frac{1}{3}$. Explain why the statement is true.

- If it is not possible to place a fraction on the chart, the team loses a turn.

- The team that makes the most "true statements" wins.

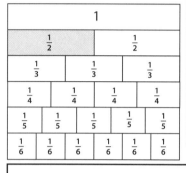

_____ $\geq \dfrac{1}{3}$	$\dfrac{1}{3} \leq$ _____	$\dfrac{3}{3} \neq$ _____
$\dfrac{1}{3} <$ _____	_____ $\neq \dfrac{2}{3}$	_____ $\geq \dfrac{1}{3}$
$\dfrac{2}{3} >$ _____	_____ $= \dfrac{1}{3}$	$\dfrac{1}{3} \leq$ _____
_____ $\neq \dfrac{1}{3}$	$\dfrac{2}{3} \geq$ _____	$\dfrac{1}{3} \geq$ _____
$\dfrac{1}{3} \leq$ _____	_____ $= \dfrac{3}{3}$	_____ $\geq \dfrac{3}{3}$

Inequality/Equality – Fourths Challenge

- Teams share a chart.
- Each team tosses a die.
- Higher number goes first.

How to Play

- Toss 2 dice. Make a fraction with the numbers tossed. Your fraction must be a **proper fraction or a fraction that equals 1.**

- Write the fraction in one of the spaces on the chart. Explain why the fraction makes the equation or inequality true.

- **Example:** Toss a 4 and a 6. Make the fraction $\frac{4}{6}$. Write the fraction in the box, $\frac{4}{6} \geq \frac{1}{4}$. Explain why the statement is true.

- If it is not possible to place a fraction on the chart, the team loses a turn.

- The team that makes the most "true statements" wins.

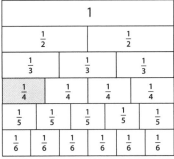

_____ $\geq \dfrac{1}{4}$	$\dfrac{1}{4} <$ _____	$\dfrac{2}{4} =$ _____
$\dfrac{2}{4} <$ _____	_____ $> \dfrac{4}{4}$	_____ $\geq \dfrac{3}{4}$
$\dfrac{3}{4} >$ _____	_____ $\neq \dfrac{3}{4}$	$\dfrac{4}{4} \geq$ _____
_____ $\neq \dfrac{4}{4}$	$\dfrac{1}{4} \leq$ _____	$\dfrac{2}{4} \geq$ _____
$\dfrac{1}{4} \geq$ _____	_____ $\neq \dfrac{2}{4}$	_____ $\leq \dfrac{3}{4}$

Inequality/Equality – Fifths Challenge

- Teams share a chart.
- Each team tosses a die.
- Higher number goes first.

How to Play

- Toss 2 dice. Make a fraction with the numbers tossed. Your fraction must be a **proper fraction or a fraction that equals 1.**
- Write the fraction in one of the spaces on the chart. Explain why the fraction makes the equation or inequality true.
- **Example:** Toss a 2 and a 4. Make the fraction $\frac{2}{4}$. Write the fraction in the box, $\frac{2}{4} \geq \frac{2}{5}$. Explain why the statement is true.
- If it is not possible to place a fraction on the chart, the team loses a turn.
- The team that makes the most "true statements" wins.

	1	
$\frac{1}{2}$		$\frac{1}{2}$
$\frac{1}{3}$	$\frac{1}{3}$	$\frac{1}{3}$
$\frac{1}{4}$	$\frac{1}{4}$	$\frac{1}{4}$ $\frac{1}{4}$
$\frac{1}{5}$ $\frac{1}{5}$	$\frac{1}{5}$	$\frac{1}{5}$ $\frac{1}{5}$
$\frac{1}{6}$ $\frac{1}{6}$	$\frac{1}{6}$ $\frac{1}{6}$	$\frac{1}{6}$ $\frac{1}{6}$

_____ $\geq \frac{2}{5}$	$\frac{1}{5} \leq$ _____	$\frac{4}{5} \geq$ _____
$\frac{5}{5} \neq$ _____	_____ $> \frac{4}{5}$	_____ $\geq \frac{2}{5}$
$\frac{4}{5} \neq$ _____	_____ $> \frac{3}{5}$	$\frac{4}{5} \leq$ _____
_____ $\leq \frac{2}{5}$	$\frac{5}{5} =$ _____	$\frac{3}{5} \geq$ _____
$\frac{1}{5} \leq$ _____	_____ $\geq \frac{3}{5}$	_____ $\neq \frac{2}{5}$

Inequality/Equality – Sixths Challenge

- Teams share a chart.
- Each team tosses a die.
- Higher number goes first.

How to Play

- Toss 2 dice. Make a fraction with the numbers tossed. Your fraction must be a **proper fraction or a fraction that equals 1.**
- Write the fraction in one of the spaces on the chart. Explain why the fraction makes the equation or inequality true.
- **Example:** Toss a 2 and a 4. Make the fraction $\frac{2}{4}$. Write the fraction in the box, $\frac{2}{4} \leq \frac{4}{6}$. Explain why the statement is true.
- If it is not possible to place a fraction on the chart, the team loses a turn.
- The team that makes the most "true statements" wins.

		1			
	$\frac{1}{2}$			$\frac{1}{2}$	
	$\frac{1}{3}$		$\frac{1}{3}$		$\frac{1}{3}$
$\frac{1}{4}$		$\frac{1}{4}$		$\frac{1}{4}$	$\frac{1}{4}$
$\frac{1}{5}$	$\frac{1}{5}$	$\frac{1}{5}$	$\frac{1}{5}$		$\frac{1}{5}$
$\frac{1}{6}$	$\frac{1}{6}$	$\frac{1}{6}$	$\frac{1}{6}$	$\frac{1}{6}$	$\frac{1}{6}$

$\underline{} \leq \frac{4}{6}$	$\frac{3}{6} \geq \underline{}$	$\frac{6}{6} \neq \underline{}$
$\frac{2}{6} < \underline{}$	$\underline{} \neq \frac{4}{6}$	$\underline{} \leq \frac{3}{6}$
$\frac{5}{6} \geq \underline{}$	$\underline{} = \frac{6}{6}$	$\frac{4}{6} < \underline{}$
$\underline{} \neq \frac{2}{6}$	$\frac{3}{6} \leq \underline{}$	$\frac{5}{6} \geq \underline{}$
$\frac{4}{6} > \underline{}$	$\underline{} = \frac{3}{6}$	$\underline{} \leq \frac{4}{6}$